PUFFIN BOOKS

RICHIE RICH

Richie knew his mother meant well, but she still didn't get the idea. 'My friends at school are always too busy to come over,' he said. 'So I thought —'

Before he could get the words out, Cadbury's pocket organizer began to beep.

'I'm sorry to interrupt, Master Rich,' the butler said, 'but it's time for your chemistry lesson with Professor Keenbean.'

Richie's shoulders sagged. 'Do I *have* to?'

'We must keep to our schedule, sir,' Cadbury reminded him.

'Our schedule,' Richie nodded glumly. 'Sure.' He followed the butler out. He seemed to be scheduled for *everything*, except having friends.

Todd Strasser has written many award-winning novels for young and teenage readers. He speaks frequently at schools about the craft of writing and conducts writing workshops for young people. He and his wife and children live in Westchester County, New York. They don't have a tree-house.

CW00952486

Macaulay Culkin

Richie Rich

Todd Strasser

Based on the screenplay by
Tom S. Parker & Jim Jennewein
Based on a story by Neil Tolkin
Based on the characters appearing
in Harvey Comics

PUFFIN BOOKS

PUFFIN BOOKS

Published by the Penguin Group
Penguin Books Ltd, 27 Wrights Lane, London w8 5tz, England
Penguin Books USA Inc., 375 Hudson Street, New York, New York 10014, USA
Penguin Books Australia Ltd, Ringwood, Victoria, Australia
Penguin Books Canada Ltd, 10 Alcorn Avenue, Toronto, Ontario, Canada m4v 3b2
Penguin Books (NZ) Ltd, 182–190 Wairau Road, Auckland 10, New Zealand

Penguin Books Ltd, Registered Offices: Harmondsworth, Middlesex, England

First published by Puffin Books as a film tie-in 1995
1 3 5 7 9 10 8 6 4 2

Filmset by Datix International Limited, Bungay, Suffolk
Printed in England by Clays Ltd, St Ives plc
Set in 12/14 pt Monophoto Palatino

To Max and Jack Warner

Richie Rich, the richest boy in the world, stepped up to the plate. He was wearing a spotless red baseball uniform and a baseball cap with the gold letters RR above the bill. Richie tipped up the cap and brushed his straight blond hair out of his eyes. Then he popped a piece of Bubblicious bubblegum in his mouth, picked up his bat and crouched over the plate.

The plate was round and had a gold and blue rim. It was from one of Mrs Rich's old china sets.

'OK, Mr Jackson, give me the cheese,' Richie shouted. Mr Jackson the famous Yankees hitter, was a good friend of Richie's father, Richard Rich, the wealthiest man in the world. They were playing ball on the Riches' lawn, a seemingly endless expanse of perfectly trimmed grass dotted with statues and fountains.

'Don't drop the elbow,' said Jackson, who was standing a little way from Richie. He had come by to give Richie some batting tips. 'Take a nice level swing.'

'Thanks, Reggie,' Richie said.

He swung.

Crack! The ball shot across the lawn and through the legs of Ethel, one of the maids, who was standing in the outfield wearing a black and white uniform and a baseball mitt.

Richie sighed. He appreciated the fact that the family servants had come out to play baseball with him on the front lawn, but it would have helped if they knew something about the game.

Richie turned to the catcher, who was actually the family butler and Richie's personal valet. His name was Cadbury, and under the catcher's gear he wore a white bow tie and a formal black jacket.

'You sure none of the kids from school could come over?' Richie asked.

'I'm quite sure, Master Rich,' Cadbury replied in his stiff English way. 'I rang them all and everyone was busy.'

'Oh, well, thanks anyway,' Richie said, and looked back at Jackson, who had the ball again. 'Put some heat on it this time, OK?'

The baseball star nodded and threw another pitch.

Crack! Richie smashed this one into the outfield. Charles, the family chef, started to back-pedal. He stretched up to catch the ball, but it bounced off his mitt and splattered into the mermaid fountain

Splash! Charles fell in after it. Dollar, Richie's

black and white dog, fished the ball out of the fountain and started to run towards them. Richie smiled weakly at Cadbury.

'Good clubbing, Master Rich,' the butler cheered, obviously trying to lift the boy's spirits. 'You're scoring loads of points.'

'They're called runs, Cadbury,' Richie corrected him.

Under the butler's chest protector, something started beeping.

'Runs,' Cadbury repeated, pulling a pocket-sized digital organizer out of his pocket and looking at it. 'Yes, of course. And I'm afraid *run* is what we must do.'

Richie winced and wondered if every kid's life was scheduled as tightly as his. 'Can't I have one more innings?' he begged.

'That really isn't possible, sir,' Cadbury replied, removing his mask and chest protector. 'It's time for your presentation.'

The butler pointed up into the sky, where a large blue helicopter was approaching. Richie nodded sadly and handed his bat to Cranston, the footman, who wiped it carefully with a towel.

'Thanks, Mr Jackson.' Richie shook Reggie Jackson's hand.

'Any time,' the famous hitter said.

'Really, Master Rich,' Cadbury said, 'we must be going.'

Richie nodded wistfully and followed the butler back towards the large white mansion where he and his family lived.

A little while later Richie and the butler boarded the helicopter. Cadbury settled into one of the soft leather seats and looked across at Richie, now dressed in a neatly pressed blue three-piece suit. Richie gazed forlornly out of the window as the engines roared and the helicopter lifted off the ground.

Cadbury felt a pang in his heart for the boy, whom he had known since birth. He could still recall that cold and frosty November morning twelve years before. He and the other servants had stood at the bottom of the great staircase waiting anxiously, while upstairs Mrs Rich gave birth to her first and only child.

Suddenly Mr Rich, a robust and handsome blond-haired man, had burst out of the upstairs bedroom with a broad smile on his face. He'd stood at the top of the stairs and announced to the crowd below that he now had a son! And Cadbury, along with all the other servants, had cheered with genuine happiness.

Now Cadbury glanced to the other side of the helicopter where there sat a brawny man wearing a slightly wrinkled brown suit. He had short brown hair and his right eye twitched nervously. His name

4

was Ferguson and he was the chief of security for the Rich family.

It had always struck Cadbury as sad that a boy of Richie's age required constant security. But rarely had a child been born into a life of such wealth and privilege. It was an unfortunate fact that families such as the Riches were often the target for a criminal element bent on separating them from their money.

From the moment he was born, Richie had had an unusual upbringing. Instead of animals hanging from the mobile over his cot, there had been foreign currencies. And as a baby he had been cared for by any number of servants and baby nurses. Many parents might have taken advantage of so much help. But Mr and Mrs Rich spent every spare second with their son, playing and reading and making him feel like *he* was their most valued treasure. And as a result, Richie was a remarkably good-natured and unspoiled young man.

In the helicopter, Richie gave Cadbury a puzzled glance, as if wondering why the butler was staring at him. Cadbury averted his eyes. Richie had grown up to be a young man with a sweet disposition, a spirited sense of play, and a genuine caring for others. Quite unusual for a boy who could have anything he wanted, and *everything* money could buy.

But still, it was not the easiest life. As the

helicopter descended towards a large industrial factory, Cadbury watched the boy bite his lip nervously. Master Rich was learning that his world of unimaginable luxury brought with it responsibilities far beyond those of any normal child.

2

The sound of the approaching helicopter made Gloria Koscinski look up in the air. Helicopters weren't something she saw everyday, especially over the dusty, weed-filled baseball field where she and her friends played each afternoon.

Gloria was a fiery, red-headed twelve-year-old who might have been very pretty if she'd bothered to brush her hair and dress in anything except jeans and T-shirts. But being comfortable and playing baseball was far more important to her than looking pretty.

'What's goin' on?' asked her friend Tony, a thin black-haired kid wearing wrap-around sunglasses.

'A helicopter's coming,' said Peewee, a big Eurasian kid who was munching on some French fries.

'We know that, dummy,' said Omar, an African-American boy with short spiky dreadlocks.

'That's Richie Rich's helicopter,' Gloria said. 'I seen it on TV.'

'Richie who?' asked Tony.

Gloria scowled at him. 'What planet you been

7

living on? Richie Rich is the richest kid in the world.'

'He's got his own helicopter?' Tony asked in wide-eyed wonder.

'He's got his own *everything*,' said Omar, eyeing Peewee's bag of fries hungrily. Thinking of a way to distract the big kid so he could grab a couple of fries, Omar pointed at the United Tool factory across the street. A large crowd of employees was grouped at the factory gates, where a woman in a bright red dress was standing on a podium with a microphone. Half a dozen news photographers and TV news crews were mixed into the crowd.

'Look, Gloria,' Omar said, pointing at the crowd. 'Your mom's gonna make a speech.'

While everyone looked at the crowd, Omar reached towards Peewee's bag and tried to filch a few fries.

'Hey!' Peewee shouted and yanked the bag away. 'You wanna die young?'

Omar backed away, shaking his head.

'Who cares about speeches and helicopters,' Tony said. 'Let's play ball.'

'Yeah, come on,' said Peewee. 'None of us is ever gonna fly in a helicopter so it don't matter.'

Inside the helicopter, Ferguson, the chief of security, reached up and flicked on a small television. On the screen the face of a newswoman holding a micro-

8

phone appeared. Richie could see the gates of the United Tool Company in the background.

'Today marks a miracle of sorts here at the United Tool Company,' the newswoman was saying. 'Just a few weeks ago this factory was bankrupt, and six hundred workers had lost their jobs. But today they're celebrating a new lease of life, courtesy of billionaire businessman and philanthropist Richard Rich.'

'You should be proud,' Cadbury said to Richie.

Richie nodded and continued watching the television. He could see the helicopter in which he was riding begin its landing.

The newswoman continued to speak over the growing roar of the helicopter: 'And now, Richard Rich, the man who has made it his personal crusade to revitalize industrial America, is about to appear.'

The helicopter bounced slightly as it landed. Richie stared through the window at the crowd of news people and tool company employees pushing forward. Then he started to get up.

'Wait a second.' Ferguson held up his hand and went out of the door first. He was checking to make sure everything looked safe. 'OK, you can come out.'

Richie took a deep, nervous breath and walked to the door of the helicopter. A few flashes went off, but most the photographers lowered their cameras and frowned.

'Uh, hi, everyone,' Richie said, smiling and waving. 'My dad couldn't make it so he sent me instead.'

The photographers' cameras started flashing. The woman wearing the bright red dress and big flashy bracelets stepped up to Richie and offered her hand.

'Welcome to United Tools, Richie,' she said. 'My name's Diane Koscinski, and I'm the union rep. I'll be making the presentation today.'

They shook hands. 'We're so glad you could come,' Diane said.

'Me, too,' said Richie. 'It's a big thrill.'

He noticed that Diane was giving Cadbury a funny look, as if wondering what he was doing there.

'This is Cadbury,' Richie said.

'I'm Master Rich's personal valet,' Cadbury added.

'A valet, huh?' Diane said, offering her hand. 'Never met one of your type.'

'That does not surprise me, madam,' Cadbury replied with a stiff bow, but not shaking the woman's hand.

Richie hoped that Mrs Koscinski wasn't insulted. It would be difficult to explain that Cadbury had a thing about flashy colourful clothes. Now Diane turned to the podium and spoke to the crowd.

'Fellow workers,' she said, 'it's not just this company that owes Mr Rich its thanks, but this whole town. So to mark this special morning, the first day of the reorganization that's gonna bring our jobs back, we're gonna ask Richie to accept this gold-plated United Tool socket wrench set for his dad.'

The crowd burst into applause as a little girl in a pink dress presented Richie with a set of gold-plated wrenches on a red satin pillow. Richie, however, hardly seemed to notice. He was staring at the kids playing baseball in the dusty lot across the street. They were yelling and running around and having a great time.

'Ahem.' Cadbury cleared his throat and nudged Richie, who looked down at the gold wrenches.

'Oh, uh, yes.' Richie turned to the microphone. He planned to give a little speech, but he'd become so distracted by the kids playing ball that he forgot it. 'Uh, I'd just like to say, on behalf of my dad, thanks for the wrenches. I, uh ... I know my dad loves socket wrenches ... I know I love socket wrenches ... And if my mom knew what a socket wrench was, I'm sure *she'd* love them too.'

The crowd smiled up at him and nodded approvingly. Richie scuffed his foot on the ground. 'Now, I'd really like to stay, but I gotta get back home and do my homework. It's been real —'

The crowd pressed forward, as if not wanting to let him leave. But Richie had a lot of experience with crowds and quickly slipped through them and headed towards the lot across the street.

*

Cadbury was not surprised to find Richie with his face pressed against the chicken-wire fence, watching the kids play baseball. If anything, it saddened him. And what saddened him more was that gorilla Ferguson, who had just stepped up behind the boy.

'Excuse me, sir,' the chief of security said. 'This area isn't secure. Please return to the helicopter immediately.'

Richie shook his head. 'But I just wanted to –'

He was cut short as Ferguson grabbed his arm. 'You have to return to the –'

This was too much for Cadbury. The butler stepped in. 'Don't touch him.'

Ferguson instantly let go and backed away. There were times when Cadbury truly hated his responsibilities, and this was one of them.

'I'm sorry, Master Rich,' the butler said. 'But we must be on our way. You have a very busy afternoon.'

Richie nodded obediently and turned back towards the helicopter. Behind him, Ferguson and Cadbury glared at each other.

'It's my job to protect him,' the security chief glowered.

'Very well,' Cadbury replied calmly. 'But grab him like that again and *you'll* be the one who needs protection.'

Moments later, the helicopter lifted off. Once again, Cadbury sat across from Richie and watched as the boy stared down at the baseball game. Finally, when the field was out of sight, Richie turned to his valet.

'Sometimes I wonder what it's like, to be like them,' he said.

Cadbury knew Richie was referring to the ragtag kids who'd been playing ball. Their lives were free and unscheduled. They didn't require bodyguards and valets and servants. It was obvious to Cadbury that Richie had discovered that there was something missing from his life after all. Something no amount of money could buy.

3

Soon the vast Rich estate came into view. At its centre was the huge white mansion in the style of a French château. Behind the mansion was a large swimming-pool shaped like a dollar sign, and a tennis court. Beyond that was the race-track where Richie drove his miniature cars, and the riding stable. The estate was truly a fabulous place, filled with lots of things for a young man to do.

Richie stared down at it, but his mind was still on that dusty lot where he'd watched the kids playing. He yearned to join them.

Meanwhile, seated across from him, Cadbury was on the phone. 'Yes, Mrs Rich, we're flying over the front yard now . . . I'm sure he'll be very happy to hear the news.' He hung up the phone. 'Master Rich, your father is home from his business trip.'

For the first time since they'd boarded the helicopter for the flight home, Richie smiled. Moments later, the helicopter landed on the front lawn. Richie didn't wait for Ferguson to make sure everything was OK. He burst out of the helicopter and raced across the lawn, with Cadbury hurrying to catch up.

At the front door, Richie slid his coded keycard into a special slot, unlocking the complex security mechanism. He pushed open the door and went inside. The interior of the mansion was like a museum, filled with priceless paintings, sculpture and furniture. But all Richie saw was Dollar racing up to greet him, with his black ears flopping against his white head.

'Hey, Dollar!' Richie rubbed his head affectionately. 'Where's Mom and Dad?'

Dollar barked happily and trotted off. Richie followed. The mansion was so big that it could take forever to find someone, but Dollar always seemed to know where people were. As Richie followed, he pulled off his jacket and tossed it on to the arm of a sculpture.

Dollar led him to the living-room at the back of the mansion. There Richie saw his mother and father staring out through a large window at the back yard. They were talking and Richie didn't want to interrupt. Mrs Rich was an elegant blonde woman with a long neck and large blue eyes.

'Darling,' her husband was saying, 'when I said we should have a family portrait, this wasn't quite what I was thinking of.'

Richie peered past them and out of the window. In the distance was Mount Richmore, the family mountain. A dozen workmen were up on platforms carving huge stone portraits of the family in the face of the mountain. Another worker was below them on the ground using some sort of rock-cutting laser gun. The gun looked like a small cannon and shot a red laser beam into the rock to carve the faces. The other workmen stood on scaffolding polishing the rough rock.

'Sweetheart,' Richie's mother said. 'It wasn't my idea. Raphaella came up with it. She's the artist. Who are we to stifle her creativity?'

'How'd she do it so fast?' Mr Rich asked. 'I've only been gone for a week.'

'Professor Keenbean invented some sort of photon, er, particle . . . maximizer . . . something like that,' his wife said. 'It seems to do the job.'

'Well, you know I'm all for the arts,' Mr Rich said, 'but isn't this a tad pretentious? Our faces a hundred feet high? Wait till Geraldo gets a hold of this.'

His wife smiled. 'Oh, Richard, I really think you're over-reacting. Or is there something about it you don't like? The glasses?'

Mr Rich's forehead furrowed. 'I don't mind the glasses. But don't you think my cheeks look too puffy? I know I've put on a few pounds recently, but you have to admit, I do look puffy up there.'

'I can take care of that.' Mrs Rich turned to the phone. Richie saw his opportunity to join them.

'Hey, Dad!' He and Dollar jogged over.

'Hey, slugger, great to see you,' Mr Rich said, giving him a warm hug.

Mrs Rich put her hand over the telephone receiver and gave Richie a kiss on the cheek. 'How was the presentation at United Tool?' she asked.

'Terrific,' Richie said. 'They gave Dad a gift.'

Cadbury came into the living-room carrying the gold wrenches and a cellular phone. 'Socket wrenches, sir.'

'No kidding?' Mr Rich looked very pleased. 'How'd they know I needed a set of these?'

'And, Dad,' Richie said excitedly, 'while I was there, I saw these kids playing baseball and −'

'I'm terribly sorry to interrupt,' Cadbury said, holding the cellular phone out to Mr Rich, 'but it's the President.'

'Of which country?' Mr Rich asked, as he toyed with the ratchet from the tool set.

'Ours, sir.'

Richie's father winced. 'Probably needs another loan,' he said in a low voice as he took the phone. Then he patted Richie on the head. 'I'll just be a minute.'

Richie's father went off to another part of the room to speak to the President. Richie turned to his mother, who was also on the phone, speaking to the artist in charge of Mount Richmore.

'Yes, it's his cheeks,' she was saying. 'He feels

they're a little too puffy. Can you do something about that? A little liposuction perhaps? Thank you so much.'

Richie watched her hang up the phone and turn to a table where she was putting flowers in a vase.

'Uh, Mom?' he said. 'I was wondering, if it's OK with you, can I invite some kids over?'

'Of course, dear,' his mother replied. 'A dinner party perhaps? Just tell me how many and when, and I'll have Brenda send out the invitations.'

'Not a party, Mom,' Richie tried to explain. 'Just something —'

'Informal,' Mrs Rich said for him. 'All right. More like a buffet. We'll have it in the Oak Room. That should be large enough to accommodate your friends from school.'

Richie knew his mother meant well, but she still didn't get the idea. 'My friends at school are always too busy to come over,' he said. 'So I thought —'

Before he could get the words out, Cadbury's pocket organizer began to beep.

'I'm sorry to interrupt, Master Rich,' the butler said, 'but it's time for your chemistry lesson with Professor Keenbean.'

Richie's shoulders sagged. 'Do I *have* to?'

'We must keep to our schedule, sir,' Cadbury reminded him.

'Our schedule,' Richie nodded glumly. 'Sure.' He

followed the butler out. He seemed to be scheduled for *everything*, except having friends.

Cadbury made sure Richie arrived on time at Professor Keenbean's laboratory, located in the left wing of the mansion. Then he returned to the living-room, where Mr Rich was just getting off the phone with the President.

'I'm afraid I've got bad news, honey,' Mr Rich was saying.

Mrs Rich looked up from her flowers with a pained look on her face. 'Don't tell me you're flying out again.'

Mr Rich nodded. 'I'm sorry, darling. Tonight, after dinner.'

'But you just got in,' Mrs Rich said. 'We were supposed to spend some time together.'

Mr Rich took her in his arms and hugged her apologetically. 'I'm sorry. How do you put up with me?'

'Well,' his wife said with a teasing smile. 'You *do* have seventy billion dollars.'

Cadbury stood by quietly. He was aware that some people might find such a comment terribly shocking, but Mrs Rich was only kidding.

'Is that the *only* reason?' Mr Rich asked his wife in jest.

4

Chemistry was probably Richie's least favourite subject, so he was fortunate that his father had hired Professor Keenbean. Of course, the scientist did other things besides tutor Richie. As Richie walked into the lab he saw the Professor speaking before a video camera being held by one of his assistants. Nearby, Ferguson, the security chief, stood and watched.

The Professor was a chubby man whose belly pressed against his white lab coat. His frizzy brown hair stuck out from his head and he wore thick glasses. He was always eating.

'You stockholders are now looking at the twenty-first century's answer to the problem of waste management here at the Rich Industries Research and Development lab,' Professor Keenbean was saying. Behind him a huge bucket, eight feet across, was suspended above the floor on an overhead conveyor belt. As the Professor spoke, the bucket moved towards a dumpster-size machine called the Sub-Atomic Molecular Reorganizer.

The huge bucket stopped over the gaping mouth of the Reorganizer and its hinged bottom creaked open, dumping a variety of recyclable items like old tyres, aluminium cans, plastic milk bottles and glass jars into the machine.

Siiiisssssss! The machine began to hiss and whine, and a fiery white light shot up from inside. Professor Keenbean moved to a control board and punched some buttons on a keypad. Richie heard more strange sounds, which he assumed were being made by molecules being wrenched apart and recombined.

'Useless garbage is quickly broken down into basic molecular components,' Professor Keenbean went on, 'then recombined into a whole range of useful products – from bedpans to bowling balls. Hey, need a new bedpan? I sure do.'

The Professor typed the word BEDPANS into the machine. Then he walked to the end of the machine and stopped at a small door where new products rolled out. Richie noticed that Ferguson was paying special attention to how the Sub-Atomic Molecular Reorganizer worked.

'It's quick, it's easy,' he said to the camera as he lifted the new product. 'In no time at all we've turned fifteen pounds of yesterday's trash into a beautiful . . . bowling ball?'

Professor Keenbean stared at the bowling ball that had just rolled out of the small door. 'Yes, a thoroughly useful bowling ball.'

He tried to lift the ball off the conveyor belt, but could hardly make it budge. 'Oh, dear, it weighs a ton!' He finally managed to slide it off.

Crash! The ball fell to the floor and shattered into a million tiny pieces.

Professor Keenbean turned to the camera. 'Cut! Cut!'

'Still not working, is it, Professor?' Richie asked.

'Oh, hello, Richie,' the Professor said. 'Not working? Hardly. It just has a few kinks that need ironing out. Not to worry. Ready for your chemistry tutorial?'

'To tell you the truth, I'm really not in the mood,' Richie replied. 'What else are you working on?'

Keenbean picked up a half-eaten liverwurst sandwich and they started to walk through the lab, passing scientists in white coats working on a variety of experiments. Here and there were tall shelves filled with all sorts of inventions, and in one corner of the lab was a large laundry basket filled with dirty labcoats and towels.

Two scientists were standing next to a wall painted with sticky black goo. A TV set, a chair and a bowling ball were stuck to it. Groaning together, the scientists lifted a weight marked '200 LB' and stuck it to the wall.

'Wow,' Richie gasped.

'It's a new adhesive,' Professor Keenbean explained through a mouthful of liverwurst. 'A hundred times stickier than the strongest adhesive known to man. I call it Cementia. Oh, and wait till you see what's over here.'

The Professor gestured excitedly with his arm and accidentally knocked one of the scientists into the black goo on the wall.

'Help!' the poor man shouted as other scientists tried to prise him off the wall. Meanwhile, Professor Keenbean continued towards the next experiment: a male mannequin dressed in a grey suit.

'Now *this* could be the biggest thing since your father and I invented the micro-chip and the ice-cream sandwich,' Professor Keenbean said, picking up a spray can and spritzing the suit with a colourless spray. 'It makes any fabric instantly impervious. Dirtproof, stainproof and waterproof.'

Blam! Richie ducked at the sudden sound of a gunshot. Looking up, he watched amazed as an assistant lowered a smoking rifle. Professor Keenbean walked up to the mannequin and pulled a bullet out of the suit.

'Did I mention bulletproof?' the Professor asked, proudly holding up the bullet. 'Works every time.'

Clang! Just then the front of the suit ripped away from the rest of the fabric and clattered stiffly to the floor.

'We are trying to work out one small side-effect,' Professor Keenbean admitted. 'Not only does the fabric *act* like a suit of armour, but it weighs about the same as well.'

Richie smiled and turned to yet another experiment: two bees in a small glass box. 'What are these? Bees?'

'Not just bees, I call them Robo-bees,' Professor Keenbean explained, picking up a remote control device with switches and dials on it. 'These little guys emit pheromones that attract real honey bees who'll follow them to the field the farmer wants pollinated.'

He handed the remote control to Richie. 'Here, take one for a test flight.'

Richie made the Robo-bee hover, then turn left and right and fly in a circle. 'This is amazing!'

'Teams of scientists worked night and day for five years perfecting its micro-circuit technology,' Professor Keenbean said proudly. 'Millions and millions of dollars were spent on that one bee alone.'

Just then Cadbury entered the lab carrying a tray with a silver pot and tea cups. 'Your afternoon tea, Master Rich.'

Noticing the bee, Cadbury put down the tray and picked up a folded magazine.

Splank! Before Richie or Professor Keenbean could stop him, Cadbury whacked the tiny electronic bee, then turned crisply and left. Richie and the Professor stared down at the mangled bee with their mouths agape.

'I don't believe it!' Professor Keenbean cried.

At dinner-time that evening, a black limousine snaked its way up the long driveway that led to the Riches' mansion. Seated in the back was Laurence Van Dough, a cold calculating businessman dressed in a dinner jacket. Van Dough was an employee of Mr Rich's, but he intended to change that soon. All he needed was a certain piece of information, and he hoped to get it that night.

The limousine came to a stop in front of the mansion. Van Dough pushed open the door and stepped out ... *splat!* right into a mud puddle. Van Dough stared down at his muddy shoe and felt his blood begin to boil. He looked up at the chauffeur.

'Thirty-six-and-a-half miles of driveway and you park in the five feet with a puddle,' he grumbled.

'I'm very sorry, sir,' the chauffeur replied.

'Sorry doesn't cut it,' Van Dough growled. 'After tonight, find another job.'

Van Dough patted his bald head with a handkerchief and walked towards the front door. Ferguson, the chief of security, joined him.

'Good evening, Mr Van Dough,' he said loudly. 'Nice to see you again.'

Then, in a quiet voice, Ferguson added, 'I checked their schedule. I got a perfect time for us to do it. When they all go to England for the Queen's birthday.'

'Not here, you moron,' Van Dough hissed through clenched teeth. 'We'll talk later.'

Ferguson skidded to a stop while Van Dough kept walking towards the door. There he was greeted by a servant and led into the main dining-room. Van Dough could never quite get over the size of the Riches' dining-room. It was as large as a train station. The dining-table itself was almost the length of a football field.

Soon he found himself sitting with Mr and Mrs Rich at one end of the table, while Richie sat at the other end.

'Please excuse me, Laurence,' Mrs Rich said, picking up a phone and dialling.

At the other end of the table a phone rang and Richie picked it up. 'Hello?'

'Richie, dear,' his mother said into the phone, 'are you sure you don't want to eat with us?'

'It's OK, Mom,' Richie replied. 'I don't like that guy.'

'Neither do I,' his mother said quietly into the phone. Then in a louder voice she said, 'But *foie de veau* is very good for you.'

'So tasty too,' Richie replied, slipping the liver to Dollar under the table.

Meanwhile, Van Dough was doing his best to ingratiate himself to the host and hostess. 'The texture of this vegetable terrine is exquisite. And to combine it with this *piquante* sauce is divine!'

'Well, I'll be sure to let the cook know,' Richie's mother replied, not taken in by the compliments. She knew a phoney when she saw one, and Van Dough was *definitely* a phoney.

'Laurence,' Richie's father said. 'Let's get back to our discussion about charitable contributions.'

'Yes,' Van Dough said. 'Your donations are costing the corporation over a billion dollars a year, sir. I just think it's time we asked ourselves, what are we getting for that?'

'What are *we* getting?' Mrs Rich seemed puzzled and annoyed. 'We're getting homeless shelters and food banks and medical clinics for poor children.'

'Now, darling,' Mr Rich said. 'Laurence's job is to keep an eye on the bottom line –'

'Which is why I also oppose this United Tool acquisition,' Van Dough said. 'We should be getting rid of dead weight, not acquiring it.'

'I totally agree,' Mr Rich said. 'That's why I'm getting rid of United Tool.'

His wife looked shocked. 'But all those people . . . Their jobs.'

'Brilliant,' Van Dough said. 'Why didn't I think of that? We buy the property in bankruptcy, level the factory, subdivide and –'

'No, Laurence,' Mr Rich said. 'I'm keeping the factory open, like I said I would.'

Van Dough thought he understood. 'We bust the union and slash benefits, then sell the company.' But the look Mr Rich gave him said he was wrong again. 'Er, we don't sell the company?' he guessed sheepishly.

'We give it to the workers,' Mr, Rich said.

'*Give* it?' Van Dough repeated, dumbstruck.

'Absolutely,' Richie's father said. 'We modernize, of course, retool, then turn control of the factory over to the workers. *They* know the business better than we do. Let them run it.'

'Oh, Richard,' his wife gushed. 'That's a wonderful plan.'

They both turned to Van Dough to see his reaction. 'Oh, yes,' he said drolly. 'Simply wonderful.'

Suddenly the doors to the dining-room burst open and Professor Keenbean dashed in carrying a box. 'Mr Rich! I've done it! I've perfected the —' He stopped and hungrily eyed the food on the table. 'Oh, you're dining.'

But Richie's father was already on his feet. 'Fantastic, Keenbean, let's see it!'

Professor Keenbean took the device out of the box. It looked like a Flash Gordon ray gun. Richie, always curious about new inventions, came from the other end of the table to look at it.

'Behold, the Smellmaster,' Mr Rich said proudly, showing it to his wife. 'Look at this, darling. We've got eyeglasses to see better, hearing aids to hear better . . . Shouldn't we have something to *smell* better?'

'We do, dear,' his wife replied. 'It's called Chanel.'

'Yes,' said Mr Rich. 'But the Smellmaster Nine Thousand converts any smell within twenty yards into a digital audio signal. Here, Rich, you do the honours.'

Richie aimed the Smellmaster at a glass of wine. 'Wine,' the Smellmaster said in a computerized voice. 'Petit Syrah, 1974.'

Grinning, Richie aimed it at some flowers. 'Roses,' the machine announced. 'Hilversum demi-bloom. Fresh cut.'

'Keenbean,' Mrs Rich gushed, 'that's marvellous!'

Richie aimed the machine at Dollar, who was still licking his chops from dinner. 'Calves' liver,' said the machine.

Van Dough suppressed a smile. Served the brat right. Meanwhile Richie quickly handed the machine back to his father, while his mother gave him a suspicious look. 'Better make some adjustments, Dad. This thing's way out of whack. Er, can I be excused?'

Richie took off before his mother could lecture him about not eating his liver. Good riddance, thought Van Dough. He turned to his employer.

'You see, Mr Rich,' he said, 'this is precisely what I was talking about before. Toys such as these cost –'

'Toys!?' Mr Rich cut him short. 'Good Lord, man, this may just be a toy to you, but to me it represents good old-fashioned American know-how and ingenuity. And Professor Keenbean here, he's a prime example of the pioneering spirit which made this country what it is today!'

Van Dough turned to that idiot Professor Keenbean, who had seated himself at the dinner-table and started to stuff his mouth with food. The Professor looked up and smiled ... with a roll in his mouth.

After dinner, Mr and Mrs Rich escorted Van Dough into the foyer to say goodbye. The executive had not been able to get the information he needed, and he knew this might be his last chance. He pointed at a new painting on the wall.

'I see you've added a Monet,' he said. 'You know, with all the priceless works of art you have here, perhaps you should beef up your security system.'

'Nothing to worry about,' Mr Rich said. 'All our real valuables are stored in the family vault.'

'Real valuables?' Van Dough swallowed back his eagerness to learn more. 'Well, that must be some vault. I'd love to see it some time.'

'Some day I'll take you on a tour,' Mr Rich said, clapping him on the back.

Van Dough fought the desire to smile. 'I'd like that.'

They saw him to the door. Outside, Van Dough

practically kicked up his heels. The family vault! That was just what he wanted to know!

After Van Dough left, Mrs Rich felt a pinprick of uneasiness that made her turn to her husband

'Darling, what is it?' Mr Rich asked.

'Watch him, Richard,' she warned softly. 'I don't trust him.'

But her husband smiled. 'Laurence isn't so bad, honey. A little over-zealous at times, but –'

Mrs Rich just sighed. She knew her husband tried hard to see the good in everyone, but this time she was afraid he was wrong.

'Call it a woman's intuition,' she said, 'but . . . just watch your back.'

5

Later that evening, Mr Rich left for Washington on his private 727 jet. The next morning Richie was standing at the mirror in his bedroom tying his school tie when he noticed a slightly raised red spot on his chin. In a panic, he raced across the room to his computer and said, 'Computer, locate Dad.'

'Data restricted,' the computer replied electronically. 'Enter secret password.'

Richie quickly typed 'Slugger'.

'Access approved,' the computer said. 'Locating father now.'

A map of the world appeared on the computer screen and a red light flashed in the spot where Washington DC was.

In the office of the President of the United States, a small cellular phone in Mr Rich's pocket began to beep. 'Pardon me, Mr President,' he said, taking it out. 'It's my Dadlink.'

'Dadlink?' the President scowled.

'My personal communications link with my son,' Mr Rich explained. 'Works via satellite. Finds me anywhere in the world.' He turned to the cellular phone 'What is it, Richie?'

'Hi, Dad, whatcha doing?'

'Discussing economic policy with the President,' Mr Rich said. 'Is this something important?'

'You bet,' Richie replied. 'I think I'm getting my first zit.'

Mr Rich winked at the President, who smiled back understandingly. 'We'll talk about it tonight, son.'

'OK, Dad.' Richie switched the Dadlink off. He understood that talking to the President might be a little more important than his first zit. Now Cadbury came in and helped him into his jacket.

'There,' the butler said proudly. 'The perfect picture of the proper young gentle –' he stopped as his eyes reached Richie's feet, encased in hi-top day-glo Reeboks.

'Please, Cadbury?' Richie begged.

'I'm sorry, Master Rich,' Cadbury said, shaking his head. 'Not while *I'm* your personal valet.'

A little while later Richie's limo entered the gates of the ivy-covered, ultra-exclusive Mount Exeter Academy, where the motto was 'Dignity, Decorum, Dollars'. The limo stopped and Cadbury got out and held the door for Richie, who was now wearing brown wing-tip shoes.

'Your briefcase, sir.' Cadbury handed him a briefcase and Richie headed to school.

When Richie entered the classroom, he saw that Mr Dahlren, his teacher, had already begun the day's lecture. Unlike a normal classroom, this one looked more like a law firm, with framed hunt paintings on dark mahogany-panelled walls. Students in suits and ties sat at large office desks complete with computers, phones, fax machines and Rolodexes.

'Let's move on to case study number twelve,' Mr Dahlren was saying as Richie sat down at his desk. Richie's teacher was wearing a tweed jacket and green corduroy slacks. 'Your company is in dire straits. Sales are down fifty per cent, and dividends are falling. Stockholders are demanding you resign as chairman of the board. What can you do to get the board on your side and avoid impending bankruptcy?'

The teacher looked around the room and pointed at a student with red hair and freckles. 'Reynolds?'

Reynolds was sitting with his feet on his desk, reading the *Wall Street Journal*. He looked up. 'Uh, I'll have my secretary get back to you on that.'

Mr Dahlren rolled his eyes towards the ceiling and nodded at a boy practising his golf on the carpet behind his desk. 'Elsworth. How would *you* get the board on your side?'

'Bribe someone?' Elsworth guessed.

The teacher crossed his arms and shook his head. 'Guess again.'

'Uh, bribe *a lot* of someones?' Elsworth suggested.

Mr Dahlren pointed to a young man with black hair standing behind his desk, being fitted for a new suit by a tailor. 'Reginald, perhaps *you* have a more suitable answer.'

'I'd float a rumour that we were the object of a takeover bid,' the boy named Reginald replied. 'Then, as soon as our stock went up, I'd sell.'

'That's not only unethical,' Mr Dahlren said, 'it's illegal.'

'Hey.' Reginald shrugged. 'I'm only twelve years old. I can't be held legally responsible for my actions.'

The seemingly endless talk about money and board-room politics bored Richie, who passed the time faxing funny drawings of Mr Dahlren to other students.

'Uh, Richie, perhaps you can add to that,' the teacher said.

'Well, if the firm was losing money, why couldn't all the board members take a pay cut?' Richie asked.

Snickers rippled through the classroom.

'Yeah, right,' snorted Reginald. 'Like we're gonna stay rich and powerful by voting ourselves pay cuts. Good move, Chief Executive moron.'

The class laughed and Richie felt humiliated. He'd simply expressed the way he honestly felt.

35

From Mr Dahlren's class the students moved to the gym. Donning white fencing outfits, they practised their parries and thrusts with each other. Of course, the discussion never strayed far from money.

'Long-term capital appreciation is all well and good,' Reynolds was saying. 'But not without a growth strategy.'

'Well, I've just got one word to say to you,' said Elsworth. *'Plastics.'* Then he turned to Richie. 'Richie, old boy, what do you think?'

'I think all we ever talk about is money,' Richie said. 'We should be having fun.'

The boys gave him blank looks. 'But money *is* fun,' said Elsworth.

Richie could see he wasn't getting through to them. 'Look,' he said, 'maybe you guys could come over to my place this weekend. We could just hang out, OK?'

'Hang out?' Elsworth frowned.

'Yeah, like normal kids,' Richie said.

The other boys glanced at each other and scowled.

'You're acting really weird,' Elsworth said. 'And anyway, I promised my Dad I'd go to Tokyo with him for a hostile takeover.'

Richie turned to Reynolds and gave him a hopeful look.

'Sorry,' the boy replied. 'Trustees' meeting.'

'And we have tickets to the Royal Ballet,' said Cuthbert. 'With the Princess.'

Richie nodded with disappointment. He should have known. Their lives were as scheduled as his. No one had any time to have friends.

After school, Cadbury returned in the limousine to bring Richie home. Richie sat in the corner of the limo, staring glumly out of the window while Cadbury used the car phone.

'Master Rich,' the butler said, hanging up, 'your Latin lesson has been moved back an hour. That gives you time for a quick spot of polo, a half-hour with your calculus tutor, then on to your tax law seminar.'

Richie didn't respond.

'Is something amiss, sir?' Cadbury asked.

Richie nodded. 'First my "friends" are too busy to hang out with me. Now *I'm* too busy to hang out with me.'

'Master Rich,' Cadbury said, 'you are being groomed for a life of great wealth and responsibility. Certain sacrifices *must* be made.'

Maybe, Richie thought, but that shouldn't mean he couldn't have any life at all. He'd done everything he was supposed to do. He deserved some fun. Suddenly he realized they weren't far from the United Tool Company factory.

'Cadbury,' he said. 'I'm changing my schedule.'

'But Master Rich —' Cadbury began to protest.

'No buts,' Richie said firmly, then turned to the chauffeur. 'Bascomb, make a right.'

6

Richie gave Bascomb directions to the factory, but it was the dusty baseball field he really wanted to visit. When they got there he couldn't help smiling. The same group of kids was playing ball.

'Stop here,' Richie said. As soon as the limo stopped, he jumped out and slammed the door behind him.

'Master Rich, no!' Cadbury cried through the window. 'You can't play with those children. I must protest in the strongest terms.'

'Chill, Cadbury,' Richie yelled back. 'And don't follow me!'

'But they probably haven't even been vaccinated!' Cadbury shouted.

Too late. Richie jogged on to the ball field. The kids all stopped playing and gathered around him, staring like he'd just arrived from another planet.

'Check. It. Out,' said Omar, the kid with the short dreadlocks.

'I'm Richie,' Richie said.

'We know who you are,' replied Gloria, the

spunky girl with the red hair.

'So where's the chopper?' asked Tony, the thin kid with the wrap-around sunglasses.

'Dad hardly ever lets me take the helicopter to school,' Richie said.

'No chopper to go to school in?' Peewee pretended to be aghast. 'Man, that's rough.'

The kids laughed. Richie shrugged. He was prepared to take a little ribbing.

'So I was wondering,' he said, gesturing at a bat lying on the dusty ground. 'Think I could play with you guys?'

The kids exchanged looks with each other. Then, in unison, they shook their heads and said, 'Nahhhhh.' Before Richie could say anything more, they returned to their positions in the field.

'C'mon,' Richie implored them. 'Let me hit.'

'Forget it. You probably couldn't hit a beach ball,' Gloria said as she walked back to the pitcher's mound.

'Could too,' Richie said.

Gloria stopped and glared at him with her hands on her hips. 'You think you're so hot? Put your money where your mouth is.'

'You mean bet?' Richie asked, surprised.

'Yeah,' Tony shouted from second base. 'Five says she puts you away.'

'Five? No way.' Gloria shook her head. 'How about ten?'

40

Richie frowned. 'OK. Seems a little steep. But ten thousand it is.'

'Not ten *thousand*,' Gloria groaned, rolling her eyes. 'Ten *dollars*.'

'Oh.' Richie grinned sheepishly. 'You're on. Don't go away.'

Tony went around to all the kids, collecting crumpled-up dollars, quarters and loose change in his baseball hat. Meanwhile, Richie jogged back towards the limo where Cadbury waited.

'Could you loan me ten dollars?' Richie asked as he took off his jacket and handed it to the butler.

'Sir, I must say, I think it unseemly in the extreme for you to take money from these ruffians,' Cadbury replied.

Just then Tony yelled over to them. 'Hey, what are you doing? Asking the old guy for batting tips?'

'Old guy?' Cadbury repeated, raising his eyebrows. He dug into his pocket and handed Richie a ten dollar bill. 'I hope you hit a touchdown, Master Rich.'

'It's called a home run,' Richie said, returning to the field and giving Tony the money.

'It's a deal,' Tony said. He walked back to Gloria and tossed her the baseball, whispering, 'Dust him.'

'Don't worry,' Gloria replied with a wink. 'Mr Fancy Pants is going down one-two-three.'

At home plate Richie took off his suit jacket and shirt, loosened his tie and rolled up his sleeves. He

41

popped a piece of Bazooka into his mouth. Peewee, the catcher, squatted down behind him and showed Gloria a sign.

Gloria nodded. Then she wound up and fired a screamer — straight at Richie's head!

'*Ooof!*' Ducking to avoid being hit, Richie fell to the ground, kicking up a cloud of dust. The kids all laughed. But there was no way Richie would allow himself to be intimidated. He stood up, dusted off his clothes, and tapped the plate with the bat.

'C'mon, put one over,' he taunted Gloria. '*If you've got the guts.*'

Gloria's eyes widened with astonishment, then narrowed. She rocked back and hurled another screamer straight down the middle of the plate.

Crack! Richie blasted the ball high and far over the left fielder's head. The kids watched in silent amazement.

'Yes, Master Rich!' Over by the limo, Cadbury pumped his fist in triumph and did a little dance. Then he quickly caught himself and resumed his stiff, stately demeanour. 'Good show, old boy.'

Richie could see that Gloria was completely dumbfounded. One of her pitches had probably never been hit like that before.

'Lucky swing, I guess,' Richie said modestly, not wanting to make her feel bad. 'So, uh, would you guys like to come over to my house?'

'Take your money and go,' Gloria said coldly.

'I don't want the money,' Richie said.

'I said take it and leave.' Gloria glowered at him. 'You don't belong here.'

'Hey, Gloria,' Tony said. 'If he said he don't want the money . . .' Gloria stared daggers at him and Tony raised his hands to his chest and backed away. 'OK, OK, it was just a suggestion.'

Richie gazed around the field, hoping someone else might come to his aid, but none of the kids did. His shoulders sagged and he picked up his jacket and shirt and trudged back to the limo.

'A truly prodigious blow, Master Rich.' Cadbury tried to congratulate him, but Richie just got into the limo without saying a word. The butler saw how upset the boy was. Cadbury looked at the kids on the field for a long time before getting into the limo. Perhaps there was something he could do.

Several mornings later the Rich family rode to their private airstrip in their limo. They were on their way to England for the Queen's birthday. Cadbury was deeply concerned about Richie. He had never seen the boy look so glum. But fortunately, he thought he knew how to help him.

The limo pulled on to the tarmac beside the Riches' private 727. A ground crew was loading baggage and gift-wrapped packages into the jet, and Ferguson, the chief of security, was overseeing them.

The limo stopped and Cadbury hopped out and opened the door. Richie climbed out without a word. Mrs and Mr Rich followed. Mr Rich was carrying the Smellmaster.

'Darling,' his wife said, 'please tell me you aren't going to give the Queen the Smellmaster for her birthday.'

'Why not?' Mr Rich asked. 'She'll get a kick out of it. Anything to get her mind off those children of hers, right, Richie?'

Instead of replying, Richie just shrugged and stared at the ground.

'Perk up, son,' his father said. 'In just a few hours you'll be enjoying tea and crumpets in Buckingham Palace.'

'Whoop-*ee*,' Richie grumbled and climbed up the ramp and into the jet. 'I'd rather be eating hot dogs at Wrigley Field.'

Now Ferguson joined Mr and Mrs Rich. 'Security check is complete, sir,' he said. 'Hope you and your family have a great time.'

'Thank you, Ferguson,' Mr Rich said, and the security man walked away towards his car. Meanwhile, Mrs Rich turned to Cadbury.

'Is Richie upset about something?' she asked.

'He tried to make friends with some children recently,' the butler replied. 'It wasn't a great success.'

Mrs Rich looked crestfallen. 'The poor dear. He must be miserable.'

44

They both gazed up at Richie, who was staring forlornly out a window of the jet.

'Might I make a suggestion, madam?' Cadbury asked.

'Certainly,' Mrs Rich replied.

'Why not let Master Richie stay here for the weekend?' the butler said. 'Young gentlemen can find the formalities of royal functions a trifle boring, whereas here I could prepare a busy schedule of distractions.'

'Cadbury, that's a lovely idea,' Mrs Rich said with delight. 'I'll go tell Richie.'

Many executives have fish tanks in their offices, but few have tanks large enough to contain sharks. One of the few was Laurence Van Dough, who enjoyed watching the vicious creatures swim hungrily around the tank. Somehow, they reminded him of himself.

Someone knocked on the door of his office at Rich Industries International. 'Come in,' he said, swinging his chair around to his desk. Ferguson stepped into the room and closed the door behind him.

'They all got on the jet,' the security chief said.

A thin smile creased Van Dough's lips. He stood up and gazed out of the window, pressing his fingertips together. 'Finally my father will have his revenge.'

'Your father?' Ferguson said.

'Forty years ago my father started this company,' Van Dough said.

'But I thought Mr Rich's father —' Ferguson started to say.

'Well, yes,' said Van Dough, 'they founded it together. Then twenty-five years ago they parted ways. My father wanted to run the business *like* a business. Mr Rich wanted to run it like a charity.' Van Dough made a face. 'Like father, like son.'

'Hey, Mr Rich ain't done too badly,' Ferguson said.

'He squanders millions and *still* makes money!' Van Dough banged his fist against the desk in frustration.

'What did your father do after he left Rich Industries?' Ferguson asked.

'He was a businessman; he started a new business,' Van Dough said. Then, in a barely audible mutter he added, 'Biochemical weapons.'

'Pardon?' Ferguson hadn't heard him.

'Biochemical weapons!' Van Dough shouted. 'How did he know they'd be banned? He got stuck with an enormous stockpile.' He calmed a bit. 'He died penniless ... and left me with nothing.'

'Nothing?' Ferguson scowled. 'I thought you had a trust fund worth ten million dollars.'

'OK!' Van Dough flared. '*Practically* nothing! Meanwhile, look at old man Rich's son. He went on to a life of unbridled power and success . . . and everything he has should be mine!'

'It looks like that's exactly what's going to happen,' Ferguson said.

'Yes.' Van Dough grinned wickedly. 'In a few short hours I'll be Chairman and CEO of Rich Industries. And then, the Rich family vault will be mine.'

7

For Richie, staying home that weekend was a mixed blessing. It was better than going to England, but not *much* better. He still had no friends to fool around with. As he stood on the balcony outside his window and looked out at the expansive grounds of the family estate, he knew how true it was that money couldn't always buy happiness.

'Excuse me, Master Rich,' Cadbury said, coming up behind him. 'Sensing you were at something of a loose end, I arranged for a little entertainment.'

Richie wasn't enthusiastic. He knew what 'a little entertainment' meant. A circus, a private rock concert, whatever.

'Sorry, Cadbury,' he said. 'I'm not really in the mood for the Vienna Boys' Choir today.'

'The choir was unavailable, sir,' Cadbury replied. 'But I did make other arrangements.'

Richie looked up at him quizzically. Cadbury pointed towards the driveway and Richie moved to another part of the balcony. Below in the driveway, a dented old station wagon had just pulled up and the kids from the baseball field piled out, followed by Diane Koscinski, Gloria's mum. Today she was wearing a bright green dress and an orange scarf. The kids stared up at the mansion in awe.

'Whoa!' Omar gasped. 'This ain't no house. This is the whole *neighbourhood*!'

'Aw, it's not so big,' Gloria said, trying not to be impressed.

'Are you kiddin'?' Tony asked, pulling up his sunglasses. 'This place probably has its own zip code.'

On the balcony, Richie turned to the butler and grinned. 'Cadbury, I owe you one.' Then he dashed downstairs and out of the front door.

'Hi!' He waved happily to the little group.

'Hey, Rich-man,' Omar said. 'We're just checking out your crib here.'

'Crib?' Richie repeated uncertainly.

'I believe that's street slang for domicile,' Cadbury said, coming up behind them. 'An idiom.'

'Whoa,' Omar bristled. 'Who you callin' an idiom?'

'And now, if you wish,' Cadbury said, 'luncheon is served.'

'Yo, *food*!' Peewee yelled. 'I like this place!'

Richie led the kids towards the house and slipped his coded keycard into a slot by the front door.

'Hey, what is this, man, an ATM or something?' Tony asked.

'Naw, it's just a keycard,' Richie explained. 'We use them instead of keys so we can change the code every once in a while.'

Richie led the kids into the house and Diane and Cadbury followed. Like most new visitors to the Rich estate, Diane Koscinski felt self-conscious and out of place.

'I hope you didn't go to too much trouble,' she said, 'with the food and all.'

'No trouble, madam,' Cadbury replied. 'Just the usual repast.'

The long dining-table was set with an array of fine china, crystal and silverware. The kids and Diane sat down with amazed looks as the servants served them. Peewee dipped his spoon into the soup, took a sip, and made a face.

'Geeze, this house is so big, the soup's cold by the time it gets to you,' he said.

Gloria's mum stifled a laugh. 'It's vichyssoise. It's meant to be served cold.'

When the soup course was over, the servants set artichokes in front of each kid. Tony frowned at Omar, who frowned back.

'They're called artichokes,' Richie explained.

'I knew that,' Gloria said with feigned sophistication. Then she leaned to Omar and whispered, 'What do you do with it?'

Omar pulled off one leaf, then another. 'Maybe there's some kind of prize inside,' he whispered, pulling more and more leaves off. But he got to the end and there was nothing. 'Whoa, it's got hair!'

A servant set a plate of raw oysters in front of Tony, who gingerly picked one up with his fork. 'Wow, looks like a giant booger.' He put it next to his nose and then pretended to blow it.

'Gross!' Gloria shouted and all the kids laughed.

'Hush, kids,' Diane said nervously. 'Behave yourselves.'

Peewee picked up an oyster with his fork and brought it towards his mouth. Everyone watched as the slimy glob got closer and closer. Driven by hunger, Peewee shut his eyes, but at the last second he chickened out and offered it to Omar.

'No way.' Omar shook his head. 'I ain't eatin' it.'

'C'mon, it's good for you,' Peewee teased.

'Get that outta my face!' Omar shoved Peewee's arm away and the oyster flew off the fork.

Splat! It hit Cadbury in the back of the neck and started to slide down his back. The butler's eyes bulged out and he just barely managed to maintain his composure. Richie quickly took the blame.

'Uh, sorry, Cadbury, I must've slipped,' he said. 'You know, maybe we'd all be happier with —'

'A more informal dining arrangement?' Cadbury guessed. 'My thought exactly.'

'OK, guys, follow me,' Richie said, getting up and heading upstairs.

'So are we gonna get some real food or what?' Peewee asked behind him.

Upstairs, Richie stopped in front of a set of large mahogany doors. 'I think you'll like this,' he said, and pushed the doors open. Inside was a room laid out exactly like a McDonald's, with servants even wearing the red and white uniforms.

Omar's jaw dropped. 'He's got his own Mickey D's!'

Everyone raced to the counters shouting their orders. Only Gloria tried to act unimpressed. 'So what?' she mumbled. 'Big deal.'

Meanwhile, somewhere over the Atlantic, the Riches' 727 was cruising at 30,000 feet. Mrs Rich, an accomplished pilot, sat in the pilot's seat, while Mr Rich was her co-pilot. Otherwise, the jet was empty.

'You are now leaving US radar contact,' a staticky voice announced over the radio. 'Donegal radar control will have you on their scope in four hours.'

'OK, darling, we're on our own,' Mr Rich said with a smile. He started to unhook his seat belt. 'I think I'll go into the galley and make some sandwiches.'

'Great idea,' Mrs Rich said. 'Just don't go sneaking any of those chocolates back there. They're for the Queen.'

'Darling, you know I'm dieting,' Mr Rich said. 'The last thing I want is chocolate.'

On his way back to the galley Mr Rich passed all the brightly wrapped gifts for the Queen. Actually, it wouldn't hurt to have just one little chocolate, would it? But which box would they be in? Just then the Smellmaster caught his eye and he had an idea. He turned it on and aimed it at one box.

'Pâté de foie gras,' the machine reported. He aimed it at another box and the machine said, 'Seventeen grain pearls.'

Next he aimed it at a pale blue box. 'Trinitrotoluene,' said the machine. Mr Rich blinked and tried it again. Again the machine said, 'Trinitrotoluene.' Mr Rich picked up the box and headed to the cockpit.

'Darling,' he said, showing his wife the pale blue box. 'There's no card on this gift. Do you know who it came from?'

'No,' said Mrs. Rich. 'Something wrong?'

'The Smellmaster says it's trinitrotoluene,' Mr Rich said. 'And if I remember correctly, trinitrotoluene's the proper name for —'

'TNT!' they both cried at the same time.

Mr Rich stared at the small blue package. 'It's a bomb!'

'Strap yourself in, darling!' Mrs Rich commanded. 'We're going to dive!'

Mrs Rich tipped the nose of the plane down and it began to scream down through the sky. While she struggled with the controls, Mr Rich started to pry open the cockpit window. A moment later, he threw the bomb out.

Ka-Boooom! A tremendous explosion rocked the jet. Inside the cockpit, Mrs Rich struggled with the controls as the plane went into a tailspin.

'Something's wrong!' she shouted. 'We're out of control!'

Mr Rich quickly stared down at the dials and gauges. 'Oh, no!' he cried. 'The explosion must have blown off the tail!'

8

After lunch Richie showed the kids his room, which contained a regulation-size basketball court. The boys quickly started taking shots. Gloria, however, was more interested in Richie's computer.

'One of the things I use it for is talking to my dad,' Richie explained. 'We call it Dadlink. It's practically the only way I ever get to talk to my dad. He's away a lot.'

'I know what you mean,' Gloria said. 'My dad lives in California and we're both on line. If we didn't have E-mail, I'd probably never talk to him.'

She looked around the room. 'He'd sure like this place, though. Must be great to have everything you want.'

'I don't know that I do,' Richie said.

Gloria turned and looked at him. For a moment Richie was worried that she wouldn't understand, but she nodded slightly and he thought maybe she did.

Then Peewee came over, dribbling the basketball. 'You guys wanna play or what?'

'You know, it's really nice out,' Richie said. 'Uh, how about we try the kid-a-pult?'

'Kid-a-pult?' Gloria repeated.

'You'll see,' Richie said, and led them outside. A few moments later they gathered in the backyard next to a large catapult. Professor Keenbean was adjusting the controls with one hand while he held a half-eaten liverwurst sandwich in the other.

'Can we use it?' Richie asked.

'Sure,' said Keenbean. 'I'll aim it.'

'You sure this thing is safe?' Peewee asked nervously. Thirty yards away a huge air-filled cushion lay on the lawn.

'Don't be a chicken,' Gloria said, climbing into the catapult. 'Fire away!'

Sproing! Keenbean fired the catapult and Gloria arced through the air and landed on the air cushion.

'Way cool!' she shouted as she bounced up. Richie was glad that she was finally starting to have fun.

'Reload! Reload!' Keenbean shouted playfully.

The other kids quickly pressed towards the kid-a-pult. 'I wanna go next!' 'No, it's my turn!' 'No, mine!'

'Don't fight,' Richie said. 'You can go as many times as you want.'

They played on the kid-a-pult for a long time, then paused for banana splits served from an ice-cream cart by a servant.

'Man,' Peewee said half-way through his ice-cream. 'This is like the best day of my life.'

'And it's not over,' Richie said.

All the kids turned and looked at him. 'You mean, there's *more*?' Gloria asked.

'Yeah,' said Richie. 'What do you say we have a motorbike race over to the roller-coaster?'

'Roller-coaster?' Omar's eyes widened.

'Dad gave it to me for Christmas,' Richie explained. 'It's pretty intense.'

'Cool!' Everyone jumped up and started to get on the motorbikes. Except Peewee.

'Hey, man,' Tony yelled, 'don't you want to come?'

'But I just ate,' Peewee said, patting his stomach.

Omar grinned. 'Man, you *always* just ate!'

While the children were off having fun, Cadbury realized it was his duty to entertain Diane, Gloria's mother. He took her on a stroll through the gardens, past endless rows of bright pink and red azaleas.

'Is Richie happy here?' Diane asked.

'Well . . .' Cadbury hesitated. '*Most* of the time.'

Diane nodded knowingly and decided not to press the point. Instead, she waved her hand around. 'This is just beautiful.'

'Yes, my mother used to think these gardens were heaven,' Cadbury said.

'We had a garden in our old house,' Diane said. 'I loved it.'

'I'm sure madam will have her garden again,' Cadbury said.

Diane stiffened. 'Look, do me a favour and *don't* call me madam. My name's Diane.'

'Very well, Diane,' Cadbury said.

'So *you* got a first name?' she asked.

'I am Herbert,' Cadbury replied.

'Herb, huh?'

'No, I am not a seasoning,' Cadbury corrected her. 'It's Herbert.'

'Gotcha,' Diane said.

Eeeiiiinyyowwnnn! The kids suddenly raced by on their motorbikes.

'Yikes!' Diane jumped and Cadbury suddenly found her in his arms. They looked at each other for a moment, and Diane smiled. Cadbury let her go.

'Please lead on, Herbert,' Diane said, still smiling.

Moments later, they heard screams in the distance. 'What's that?' Diane asked quickly.

'Not to worry, er, Diane,' Cadbury assured. 'I imagine it's the children on the roller-coaster.'

'Oh, wow.' Diane breathed easier. 'For a second I thought maybe someone was getting mauled in the zoo.'

'Hardly.' Cadbury pointed in another direction. 'The zoo is over there.'

'I should've known,' Diane said with a wry smile. 'Let's take a look, OK?'

'Certainly,' Cadbury said and led her that way.

By the time Cadbury and Diane returned from the zoo, it was late afternoon. The kids soon joined them. Peewee, Tony and Omar got in the car. Diane smiled at Cadbury.

'Well, it's been a slice,' she said. 'Maybe I'll see you again some time, huh?'

'Perhaps,' Cadbury replied stiffly.

Diane reached forward to adjust the handkerchief in the butler's breast pocket. 'When you get off the embalming fluid give me a call, *Herbert*.'

Diane got in the car, leaving Gloria standing with Richie.

'Thanks a lot for coming over,' Richie said.

'Yeah, well, it was kind of fun,' Gloria said with a shrug. Then she grinned and nudged him playfully. 'Hey, I was just kidding, you know? It was epic, Richie. And don't forget baseball practice next Wednesday at three-thirty.'

'I'll be there,' Richie said as Gloria started to get in the car.

'Hey.' Tony rolled down the window. 'What about our hundred bucks?'

Richie stared at him puzzled.

'I told you to forget about that,' Gloria hissed.

'What hundred bucks?' Richie asked.

'The penguin-looking dude said he'd give us a hundred bucks for coming out here and playing with you,' Tony said.

Penguin-looking dude? It took Richie a moment to realize he meant Cadbury. He gave the butler a look.

'I . . . uh . . .' For once Cadbury was speechless.

'What are you talking about?' Diane asked.

'Forget about it,' Gloria said. 'No one has to pay us anything. End of story. See ya later, Richie. We had a great time.'

Diane drove away and everyone waved. Then Richie turned to Cadbury.

'If sir might permit me to explain,' Cadbury said apologetically, 'I really am very sorry for any –'

Before he could continue, Ethel the maid raced from the house and whispered something in his ear. The colour instantly drained from the butler's face.

'Cadbury, what is it?' Richie asked.

'Master Rich,' Cadbury said with a quavering voice, 'it's your parents!'

Seconds later Richie dashed into his room and shouted, 'Computer, locate Dad!'

'Data restricted,' the computer spat back. 'Enter password.'

Richie quickly typed in 'Slugger' and a map of the world appeared on the computer screen. 'Father not found,' the computer reported. 'Father not found.'

'Oh, no!' Richie cried, and buried his face in his arms.

In the Rich Industries headquarters not far away, Laurence Van Dough sat down behind a broad desk with the nameplate RICHARD RICH, CHAIRMAN on it. He put his feet up on the desk and lifted a glass of champagne in the air as if in a toast.

'To the new chairman of Rich Industries International,' he said. 'Me.'

There was a knock on the door and Ferguson came in. 'Uh, Mr Van Dough, sir?'

'Come in, Ferguson,' Van Dough said grandly. 'I'm celebrating the unfortunate demise of the Riches.'

'I, er, understand,' Ferguson stammered.

'You know,' Van Dough mused. 'After I plunder the Rich family vault, I was thinking about buying a country somewhere. Nothing too ostentatious. Something small. Luxembourg, perhaps. Or Ecuador.'

'Excellent idea, sir,' Ferguson said, fidgeting. 'There's just one slight, er, complication.'

Van Dough started to frown. 'What?'

'The boy wasn't on the plane.'

Van Dough fixed Ferguson with his steely eyes. 'You said you *saw* him get on.'

'With these eyes, sir,' Ferguson said. 'And I just had them checked. Passed with flying colours.'

'You fool!' Van Dough shouted. 'You should've had your *brain* checked! After all my careful planning! Now this!'

Ferguson stood there shaking. Van Dough realized that shouting wasn't going to help. He'd just have to come up with a plan.

'Well, how bad can it really be?' he asked to himself. 'I've already eliminated the king and queen. I'm sure I'll have no trouble dealing with that helpless little prince.'

A small orange life-raft bobbed in the middle of a broad empty blue sea. In the raft, Mr and Mrs Rich sat in shredded clothes. Their faces and hands were sunburned and cracked. Mrs Rich gazed off at the endless horizon while Mr Rich fiddled with the cellular phone that was supposed to connect him to Dadlink.

'Darling, if we ever get out of this I'm going to soak for a week in a vat of Oil of Ulay,' Mrs Rich groaned. 'Is there any more Perrier?'

'Yes, but we have to ration it,' Mr Rich said. 'There's no telling how long it may take for them to rescue us.'

Mrs Rich looked up into the vast blue sky. 'Why haven't they found us yet?'

'Probably because the locator transmitter from the jet is a mile under water,' Mr Rich replied. 'And unless we see a Radio Shack soon, we can kiss off any chance of getting my Dadlink to work.'

They shared a despairing look. Then Mrs Rich's eyes narrowed. 'There's only one person ruthless enough to put a bomb on our plane. Van Dough. When I get my hands on him –'

'Now, darling, we don't know for sure,' Mr Rich replied.

'For Pete's sake,' Mrs Rich said, exasperated. 'Wake up and smell the seaweed! You should have fired him years ago!' Her husband looked surprised at her outburst and Mrs Rich quickly recovered. 'I'm sorry, dear. I just get cranky when my plane crashes.'

Mr Rich slid over and gave her a hug. 'Darling, you know I've never fired anyone in my life. And I don't intend to start now.'

'If there's one fault you have, it's that you only see the good in people,' his wife said with a sigh. 'But Laurence Van Dough . . .'

Mr Rich knew his wife was right. 'I'm sorry, honey. I guess I just wanted to give him a chance to prove he wasn't like his father. Now we know.'

Then Mrs Rich had a thought that made her shiver. 'He must've thought Richie was on the plane too.'

'I know,' Mr Rich said. 'I feel like we *have* to survive, darling. If only to warn our son that his life is in danger.'

The days passed with no word about his parents, but Richie never gave up hope. Sitting in bed one morning, he said, 'I know they're alive, Cadbury. I just *know* it.'

'Yes, Master Rich,' Cadbury replied gently from across the room, where he was laying out the boy's clothes. 'And wherever they are, I'm sure they're together and happy.'

The phone by Richie's bed rang and he answered it. 'Hello?'

'Richie, it's Gloria. I can't believe you'd close the factory.'

'Close the factory?' Richie gasped. 'What are you talking about?'

'It just happened,' Gloria said. 'My mom and everyone got fired.'

'Gloria,' Richie said, 'I had no idea this was going to happen. You have to believe me.'

'Well, it's your dad's company,' Gloria said. 'Can't you do something about it?'

'Don't worry,' Richie said, quickly jumping out of bed. 'I will.'

He hung up and turned to Cadbury. 'The tool factory's been closed down again. It was Van Dough, right?'

'I would imagine so,' the butler replied regretfully.

Richie took a deep breath. 'Come on, we're going to corporate headquarters.'

Half an hour later, the limousine pulled up in front of Rich Industries International headquarters.

Cadbury got out and held the door for Richie, who craned his neck up at the tall building and hesitated.

'Just remember,' Cadbury said encouragingly. Then he said something that Richie didn't understand.

'What's that mean?' Richie asked.

'It's Latin for, 'You have the power of your father within you.'

'Oh, yeah.' Richie grinned. 'Kind of like, "Trust the force, Luke."'

Cadbury rolled his eyes. 'Whatever, sir.'

They went inside and took the lift up. A secretary showed them into Richie's father's office, where Laurence Van Dough came around from behind Mr Rich's desk.

'Richie, Richie, Richie,' he said sadly. 'Let me express my heartfelt sympathies on your loss. We all loved your father and mother so much.'

But Richie wasn't taken in. 'What's with the armband?'

'It's a symbol of my personal grief on your parents' passing,' Van Dough said sombrely.

'My parents are alive,' Richie said firmly.

Van Dough seemed shaken for a moment, but quickly recovered. 'Yes, I pray nightly that they are. And we're doing all we can to coordinate the search efforts.'

'Why are you in my father's office?' Richie asked, looking around.

'Because running the company can be done more efficiently from here,' Van Dough replied, gesturing to a chair in front of the desk. 'Please, Richie, sit down.'

Richie went around behind the desk and sat in his father's chair.

'I meant sit here, Richie,' Van Dough said, motioning to the chair where visitors sat.

'I like this chair better,' Richie replied from his father's chair.

Van Dough forced an amused chuckle and sat down in the visitors' chair while Cadbury walked around the desk and stood beside Richie.

'Now,' Van Dough said. 'What have you come to see me about?'

'Well, until my parents come back,' Richie replied, 'I've taken a sabbatical from school. So that I can be here and run things.'

Van Dough blinked. 'Run things?' He couldn't help chuckling again. 'Richie, let me explain something to you. The job of senior officer at a multi-national corporation is very, very demanding. The business hours go *way* past your bedtime. So it's best to leave the job to an adult who's experienced in these matters. OK?'

'I don't think so,' Richie replied, swivelling in the chair and turning to Cadbury. 'By the way, Cadbury, how much stock do I own?'

'Until your parents are found, as their sole heir,

you own fifty-one per cent of the voting stock,' Cadbury replied. 'In other words, a majority.'

Van Dough had had enough. 'But you're not of legal age to exercise voting rights!' he exclaimed, standing up.

'But *I am*,' Cadbury stated. 'And, under the terms of the Rich estate, I stand in *loco parentis* and guardian *ad litem* to Master Rich. Accordingly, I give to him full proxy power and authority.'

Van Dough's face turned red and he appeared to be clenching his jaw tightly.

'So until my parents come back I guess I'm in charge,' Richie said, crossing his arms. 'And by the way, United Tool stays open.'

Van Dough left the office without saying good-bye. Richie turned to Cadbury and winked.

10

The next few days were the most hectic of Richie's life. Despite a massive search by the Coast Guard, Marines and Navy, his parents had not been found. While Richie clung to the belief that they were still alive, the demands of the family empire would not wait.

Soon his photograph began to appear on the front pages of newspapers as journalists wrote about the twelve-year-old boy who'd taken the reigns of one of the world's largest corporations. Television shows requested interviews and major news magazines prepared stories on him.

One afternoon, Richie paced back and forth behind his father's desk with a telephone pressed to his ear. He was discussing the most pressing issue in his life.

'Yes, yes, thank you, Admiral,' he said. 'And please say hello to the Joint Chiefs. I appreciate all your help in the search.'

As he hung up, Cadbury entered to office. 'Any news?'

Richie slumped in his chair, looking despondent. 'I know I shouldn't think this way, Cadbury, but what if my parents *don't* come back?'

Cadbury gave him a stern look. 'Now listen to me, young man. Over a hundred years ago my great-grandfather George Cadbury was valet and butler to the Fourteenth Earl of Dartmouth. During the terrible war of the Crimea, the Earl went missing for thirteen long months. And yet, every single day of his absence, my great-grandfather ironed the Earl's trousers, ran his bath and laid out his clothes. He never lost hope for a second that the Earl would return.'

'And the Earl came back alive?' Richie guessed hopefully.

'No,' Cadbury said. 'He'd been butchered by a marauding band of Magyars and Cossacks. *However!* The Earl had a son who carried on in his father's stead, becoming the first Duke of Marlborough. And *he* had a son, whose name was *Winston Churchill!* So you see, Master Rich, if we never lose hope anything can happen.'

'So that means we keep ironing trousers?' Richie asked, not quite understanding.

'Precisely, sir.' Cadbury nodded.

'Well, thanks.' Now Richie was certain he didn't understand, but he appreciated the butler's spirit. 'So what's on the agenda for today?'

'You're due to meet the board in five minutes,'

the butler said. 'Then you're meeting with the French Ambassador at two. I moved your two-fifteen to three-oh-five and your three-oh-five to four-thirty. Then it's on to the Ritz-Carlton for the International Monetary Fund reception.'

The thought of so many meetings was overwhelming. Richie collapsed into his chair and shook his head wearily. 'Boy, am I tired. Cadbury, I need a pick-me-up.'

'Right away, sir.' Cadbury went to a small wood-panelled refrigerator and took out a tray with a large glass on it. 'Your chocolate shake, sir. One cherry or two?'

'Two please.'

Cadbury brought him the shake and Richie took a long, delicious sip through the straw. 'Ahhh. The rewards of corporate life, eh, Cadbury?'

'Yes, Master Rich,' the butler replied, looking at his watch. 'But I'm afraid it's time for the board meeting.'

Richie got up and carried his milk shake into an adjoining room, where a dozen distinguished-looking men and women sat around a large oval table. After saying hello, Richie sat down and continued to drink his milk shake while Van Dough made a presentation concerning some of the problems facing the corporation.

'. . . and with the losses in our manufacturing division,' Van Dough was saying, 'I'm afraid this will necessitate some employee downsizing.'

Sluuurrrpppp! Richie finished his milk shake. Everyone at the table turned and stared at him.

'You mean you want to fire people?' he asked.

'Call it what you want, Richie,' Van Dough replied. 'It's our job to cut the fat. Now, let's move on to –'

'Just a minute,' Richie said forcefully. 'Mr Van Dough, my father never fired *anybody*. He always said that when people are secure in their jobs they work harder, they work happier, and they work *better*.'

Van Dough looked. The board members traded surprised looks and began murmuring to each other.

'I mean,' Richie continued, 'if we want to cut the fat . . . I say we start right here.'

Several of the more portly board members looked down self-consciously and crossed their arms over their stomachs as if to hide them.

In the days that followed, more news stories reported on Richie's remarkable management talents and his triumphs in cutting pay at the top. Richie repeatedly defeated Van Dough's attempts to fire employees and cut their benefits. Finally, Van Dough couldn't stand it any longer.

Sitting in his office with his secretary massaging his temples, Van Dough ranted, 'This kid is a menace! Today he eliminated executive parking spaces! Now I have to park with the ordinary riffraff!'

'That's really bad, sir,' said Ferguson, seated across the way.

Van Dough banged his fist against the desk. 'I said clockwise!' he shouted at the secretary. 'Massage clockwise! These migraines are bad enough without your incompetence.'

'Sorry, sir,' the secretary said in a quavering voice.

But she still wasn't doing it right. 'Oh, get out, you cow!' Van Dough screamed at her.

The secretary ran out of the office, and Van Dough turned to Ferguson. 'I've had it,' he snarled. 'It's time to put the revised plan we discussed into operation. And make sure, *this time*, the gloves come off.'

Ferguson nodded solemnly. 'Believe me, Mr Van Dough, there'll be no mistakes.'

'There better not be,' Van Dough muttered.

The orange life-raft bobbed up and down in the smooth ocean swells. Mr Rich had begun to grow a short blond beard, and his wife's hair had been bleached so much by the sun that it was almost white. They had just finished nibbling on some small damp crackers.

'Well, I'm afraid that's it, darling,' Mr Rich said sadly. 'We're out of Perrier, the caviare's gone, and there's no more melba toast.'

73

'All we have left is this bottle of Dom Perignon,' his wife said, lifting up a large dark green bottle with a gold label. 'And this Bubblicious bubblegum.'

'Richie's favourite,' Mr Rich said. They shared a wry smile. Then Mrs Rich snuggled against him, her face clouded with concern.

'I'm so worried about him,' she said. 'He's just twelve. Still a little boy.'

'Now, now, whatever happens, I'm sure he'll be fine,' Mr Rich said, trying to reassure her.

'I just wish we could've been there more for him,' his wife said. 'Maybe we could've given him more time.'

Mr Rich nodded. 'I know. And I promise you, as soon as we get back, I'm going to start spending more time with him.'

A tear ran down his wife's cheek. Mr Rich felt very bad. Suddenly, Mrs Rich straightened up and pointed at something. 'Look!'

Bobbing in the water was a white suitcase with brown leather trim and a faint brown design.

'It's my Louis Vuitton!' Mrs Rich cried with joy. 'We're saved!'

They paddled over to it and pulled the suitcase into the raft. Mrs Rich quickly opened it.

'Well, we're saved,' she said with an ironic smirk. 'My manicure kit's intact, and my dresses. The Bill Blass, the Karl Lagerfeld . . .'

'And look, honey,' Mr Rich said with the same

dark humour. 'My tux. Now we can throw a dinner party.'

Despite their dire circumstances, they couldn't help laughing. Then Mrs Rich caught sight of something else in the suitcase. He reached in and pulled out his wife's cordless electric shaver.

'Hey, now *this* is something I really can use,' he said gleefully.

'My Lady Remington?' Mrs Rich played along. 'Oh, darling, I was just getting used to your beard.'

'No, no,' her husband said. 'Don't you see? This could be the very thing that saves our lives. The *very* thing!'

He switched it on. As soon as the shaver began to hum, he started to laugh insanely. His wife watched with concern etched on her brow. 'Darling, I'm starting to think you've had *way* too much sun.'

11

The challenges of corporate life were sometimes as mysterious as they were overwhelming. Profits were up in every division of Rich Industries except the Rich Candy Bar division.

'I don't understand it,' Richie was saying over the phone to the head of the division. Scattered over the desk in front of him were several Rich candy bars, along with several of the competitor's candy bars. 'Why are profits down twelve per cent? What does research and development say about this?'

The division head started a long-winded explanation. Richie could tell the man had no answer. Suddenly the door to Richie's office burst open and Gloria and the guys rushed in.

'Gloria!' Richie cried, putting his hand over the receiver. 'Guys!'

'Hey, Richie, nice digs!' Peewee said as he unwrapped one of the competitor's candy bars and stuffed it in his mouth.

Suddenly Richie had an idea and turned back to the phone. 'Listen, I'll have to get back to you,' he said to the head of the candy division. 'My new research and development team just walked in.'

Richie hung up the phone and turned to his friends. 'I hope you're hungry, guys, because have I got a job for you!'

A little while later, Richie had yet another meeting with the distinguished board of directors. He stood at the head of the table, holding up a Rich candy bar and one of the competitor's bars. As always, Cadbury stood behind him. Van Dough sat at the opposite end of the table, sneaking peeks at his wristwatch. Any second now, he thought, and my climb to power will begin anew.

'After careful consultation with my research and development team,' Richie was saying, 'I submit to you, gentlemen, that we at Rich Candies have to increase our nuttiness quotient by fifteen per cent because we simply cannot allow the competition to be nuttier than we are.'

Around the table the members of the board nodded in approval, while at the opposite end, Van Dough shook his head in exasperation. He couldn't wait to get rid of this kid.

Suddenly the boardroom doors burst open and two police detectives in raincoats marched into the room, accompanied by two uniformed policemen. Van Dough couldn't help smiling to himself as they approached Richie's butler.

'Are you Herbert Cadbury?' one of the detectives asked.

'Why, yes,' the butler replied, frowning.

'You're under arrest.' One of the policemen spun Cadbury around and handcuffed his hands behind him.

'What is this?' Richie gasped in disbelief.

'Surely there must be some mistake,' Cadbury insisted.

Van Dough rose to his feet, pretending to be concerned. 'Officers, you can't just barge in here. What's the meaning of this?'

'We got an anonymous tip and searched the Rich mansion,' the detective said, taking a sealed plastic bag out of his pocket. Inside were some electronic components. He showed it to Cadbury. 'Look familiar?'

The butler shook his head.

'These are bomb parts,' the detective said. 'Detonation devices, found in *your* room.'

'But that's impossible,' Richie insisted.

The detective slipped his hand around Cadbury's arm and started to lead him away. 'You're under arrest for the murder of Richard and Regina Rich.'

'But I don't know what you're talking about,' Cadbury protested.

'Cadbury!' Richie cried out and tried to follow them, but Ferguson blocked his path. 'The police have to take him downtown,' the chief of security said. 'You better stay here.'

For Richie, the rest of the morning was a nightmare. As he left the Rich Industries headquarters he was bombarded with questions from a crowd of reporters asking if he really believed his parents had been murdered and that the butler did it? And how did it feel to be betrayed by the family's most trusted servant?

At home that afternoon, Richie watched on TV as Van Dough told an interviewer how saddened he was at the shocking turn of events, and how the evidence appeared to indicate that Cadbury was indeed a murderer. Somehow, Richie wasn't at all surprised when Van Dough announced that he had requested an emergency meeting with the head justice of the Supreme Court to discuss becoming Richie's legal guardian.

But the nightmare didn't end there. As dusk fell, Richie was shocked to see all the family's servants carrying suitcases and being herded into vans and driven away. Dashing back to his television, he switched on the news in time to catch a report, 'We've just gotten word that the Supreme Court has officially granted legal guardianship of Richie Rich to Laurence Van Dough, a trusted friend of the Rich family. Meanwhile, bail has been denied to accused murderer Herbert Cadbury. And, believing that Cadbury may have had accomplices, Van Dough has dismissed all the employees of the Rich family.'

So that explained why the servants were leaving with suitcases, Richie thought sadly as he patted Dollar on the head. He twisted around in his chair and glanced at his computer, which he'd left on Dadlink permanently. As it had for the past week, the computer screen flashed its hopeless message: FATHER NOT FOUND.

Richie's stomach grumbled and he realized that he hadn't eaten all day. Not that he was very hungry, but he knew he had to have something.

'Come on, Dollar,' he said, getting up, 'let's get something to eat.'

They stepped into the hall outside his room and suddenly stopped. A man in a grey uniform was up on a ladder, installing a video camera high on the wall.

'What are you doing?' Richie asked, bewildered.

'Security camera,' the men replied tersely. 'Mr Van Dough's orders.'

A security camera? Someone had to be in charge of all this, and Richie was determined to find him. As he and Dollar went downstairs and crossed the foyer, they found another security man installing another camera. The door to a room just off the foyer was open and Richie looked in.

Unbelievable! The room had been converted into

some kind of security headquarters! One whole wall was covered with closed-circuit TV monitors showing various views of the inside of the mansion. Ferguson was standing beside a console, speaking to a tall security man with short reddish-brown hair and freckles.

'Is everything in order, Zullo?' The chief of security was asking.

'Yes, sir,' Zullo replied.

'Excuse me, Mr Ferguson,' Richie said. 'What's going on here?'

'Security system, Richie,' the security chief replied. 'For your protection.'

'My protection?' Richie scowled.

'That's right,' Ferguson said. 'And until further notice, I'm afraid I can't let you out of the house. After what happened to your parents, we can't take any chances.'

The security chief reached down to pet Dollar. 'Nice doggie.'

'*Grrrrr . . .*' Dollar growled and Ferguson yanked his hand away.

'But what about the company?' Richie asked. 'What about the board meetings?'

'You won't be going to the office any more,' Ferguson informed him. 'From now on, Mr Van Dough will be running the business.'

No sooner had Richie left the control room, than

Ferguson also departed and headed for the living-room, where Van Dough stood by a roaring fire, puffing on a cigar.

'I just let the kid know the score,' the security chief said. 'Looks like things have turned out just the way we planned, eh?'

Van Dough shot him a look. 'The way *we* planned?'

'Uh, just the way *you* planned,' Ferguson quickly corrected his mistake. '*Your* scheme to take over the Rich empire was executed perfectly, and may I say –'

'*Not* perfectly,' Van Dough cut him short. 'We still don't know where the family vault is. They must have billions stashed in there. You're head of security. Where is it?'

'That's the one thing they never told me,' Ferguson admitted. 'But don't worry, sir. My men are looking for it everywhere. We're bound to find it soon.'

Little did Van Dough and Ferguson know that Professor Keenbean was sitting in his lab, listening to their conversation on his ultra-powerful wireless listening apparatus, and eating a liverwurst sandwich.

'What about that mad Professor the Riches keep around?' Van Dough was asking. 'Stringbean or Greenbean . . .'

'Keenbean,' Ferguson said. 'Claims he doesn't know where the vault is either.'

'That disgusting fat toad,' Van Dough growled.

Down in the lab, Professor Keenbean's eyes narrowed with anger at the insult. He took another bite of his sandwich and chewed it furiously.

'Oh, and what's the latest with the butler?' Van Dough asked.

'Don't worry about him,' Ferguson replied with a nasty grin. 'I've arranged it so that Mr Cadbury will soon be so overcome with remorse and guilt that he'll hang himself in his cell.'

Van Dough smiled. 'Oh, that is *luscious*.'

12

Richie had returned to his room in the vain hope that Dadlink might have found his father. But the computer continued to show FATHER NOT FOUND. Richie sat down on the bed and felt his shoulders sag. For the first time in his life he was completely alone.

Someone knocked on his door and said, 'Security.'

'Go away,' Richie said, but the door opened and two men in grey uniforms came in anyway. Both men were carrying metal detectors and they started to run them over the walls. Richie had no idea why they were doing that, and he knew it would do no good to ask. He stood up and went across the room to the window. A guard was standing outside on his balcony!

Richie pulled the curtain closed and turned away. Now he understood. He was a prisoner in his own home. Well, he didn't have to take this. Richie made a fist and stormed out of his room. He was going to find Van Dough and give him a piece of his mind.

He went downstairs and hurried down the hall towards the living-room. Suddenly a hand reached out and grabbed him.

'Mmmmuuummph!' Richie tried to shout, but a second hand was clamped over his mouth to keep him quiet.

'Hush,' a familiar voice whispered in his ear.

Richie twisted around and stared into Professor Keenbean's face.

'To the lab!' the Professor hissed.

They hurried to the lab and Professor Keenbean quickly climbed up a ladder and started rummaging through the shelves for something.

'They're planning to kill Cadbury and make it look like a suicide,' Professor Keenbean explained as he searched.

'We've got to bust him out of jail before they get him,' Richie said.

'Here it is!' Keenbean said, reaching for a large can. 'Ooops! Look out!'

The can fell off the shelf and crashed down on to a table. The top fell off and a thick white goo oozed out. Curious, Richie reached forward to touch it.

'Don't touch it!' Professor Keenbean yelled.

SSsiiiissss! The ooze began to sizzle and quickly ate through the tabletop and dripped to the floor below.

'It's just a little concoction I've been working on,' Professor Keenbean explained, climbing down from

85

the ladder. 'I call it hydrochloricdioxy-nucleocarbonium.'

Richie frowned.

'OK,' Keenbean admitted. 'The name needs work. But this baby is the *ultimate* corrosive. It'll eat clean through a Buick.'

'And prison bars?' Richie asked hopefully.

'Piece of cake,' Keenbean said with a wink.

The next morning a pizza delivery van pulled up in front of the Rich mansion. The driver was wearing sunglasses, a bright tie-dyed T-shirt, baggy jeans and day-glo hi-tops. He jumped out, opened the back doors, and took out five pizzas. A security guard questioned him carefully about why he was delivering pizzas at 8 a.m.

Just at that moment, Richie strolled out of the front door wearing his polo clothes and carrying a polo mallet over his shoulder. In one hand he carried a small brown lunch bag.

'Wait a minute!' the guard said. 'Where do you think *you're* going?'

'It's eight o'clock,' Richie replied innocently. 'My polo lesson.'

Richie started away. The guard was going to call him back, but the pizza guy stepped in his way.

'Hey, listen, dude, I got a polo lesson, too,' he said. 'So if you can tell me where Mr Van Dough is . . .'

'Van Dough ordered these?' The guard turned back to the delivery guy. 'OK, come right this way.' He led the delivery guy inside.

Meanwhile, Richie disappeared around the back of the van. He noticed a folded copy of the daily newspaper lying in the driveway and picked it up. Then he climbed into the back of the van.

The driver returned and got in. As soon as the van started to move, Richie climbed out of the back seat.

'Hey, what are you doing in here?' the driver asked.

'I need a lift,' Richie said, slipping him a hundred dollar bill.

'Anywhere,' the driver said with a smile.

Richie settled into the passenger seat and opened the paper. His jaw dropped. In the lower corner was the headline: WRECKAGE OF RICH AIRPLANE FOUND.

Richie felt his heart stop as he quickly read the story. The wreckage had been found, but there was no trace of his parents' bodies! Then they were *still* alive!

Twenty minutes later the pizza van stopped outside the city jail and Richie hopped out, now dressed in the delivery guy's hip-hop clothes.

'How do I look?' he asked the delivery guy, who was now wearing the polo clothes.

'You'd have one heck of a time getting into the

country club, dude,' the delivery guy said with a grin.

Richie waved goodbye and climbed the stone steps towards the city jail. He went inside, where a sergeant sat at a tall desk, writing something.

'Uh, excuse me,' Richie said, and the sergeant looked up.

'Whataya want?'

'My uncle's in here,' Richie said. 'He's got very sensitive teeth and I wanted to make sure he had his special toothpaste.'

Richie held up the paper bag.

'Who's your uncle?' the sergeant asked.

'Herbert Cadbury, sir.'

The sergeant gave him a suspicious look. '*Your* uncle is Herbert Cadbury?'

'Yes, sir.'

'Lemme see that.' The sergeant grabbed the back from Richie and opened it. A tube of toothpaste, a toothbrush and a greetings card fell out on the desk. The sergeant picked up the card and looked at what Richie had written inside. 'What's this?'

'Latin,' Richie said.

'Latin?' the sergeant scratched his head, puzzled.

'It's just a little note telling Uncle Herbie I love him and also to remind him of the importance of proper dental care,' Richie explained.

The sergeant gave him a sceptical look and unscrewed the top of the toothpaste tube. Richie held his breath as the policeman sniffed the white paste inside and started to squeeze, some into his hand.

'Wait a minute!' Richie had to distract him. He pointed at a 'Wanted' poster on the wall behind the desk. 'I just saw that guy down at the corner!'

'What guy?' The sergeant turned and looked at the poster. 'You saw *that* guy?'

'Yes!'

'Hey, Marty!' the policeman called. 'Get over here!'

Another cop ran out of the back of the station. 'What?'

'The kid said he just saw this guy!' the sergeant said, pointing at the poster.

'This guy?' Marty asked, ripping the poster off the wall.

'Yeah, that guy,' the sergeant said, absent-mindedly screwing the cap back on the tube.

Marty turned and showed the poster to Richie. 'You saw *this* guy?'

Richie squinted more closely at the poster. 'Gee, the guy I saw didn't have a tattoo. Sorry.' He turned back to the sergeant and pointed at the bag. 'But you'll see that Uncle Herbie gets that?'

'All right, kid, sure,' the sergeant said.

Cadbury was standing near the bars of the cell he shared with several criminal types.

'I'm an innocent man,' he said.

'Yeah, sure,' chuckled a man with several broken teeth. 'And I'm a Supreme Court Judge.'

The others laughed.

'You'll see,' Cadbury said. 'Any second now the authorities will come to their senses and order me released.'

The words were hardly out of his mouth when a guard came along and called out, 'Herbert Cadbury?'

'See?' Cadbury turned to his cellmates. 'Gentlemen, it's been a pleasure sharing your fine company. But now it's time to rejoin the human race.'

But instead of opening the cell, the guard slid the toothpaste carton through the bars. 'Your nephew brought you this. It's for *sensitive* teeth.'

'He's got sensitive teeth!' the man with the broken teeth shouted. Cadbury's cellmates burst out in laughter. The butler clutched the bag tightly. It must have been from Richie!

Later that day another guard came along, banging the bars of the cells with his night stick and saying, 'Bathroom time, Cadbury! Ten minutes to attend to your personal needs.'

Moments later Cadbury went into the bathroom, and stood at the sink. He wet the toothbrush under the tap and then squeezed some of the thick white goo on to it. Suddenly he caught sight of his haggard, unshaven reflection in the mirror.

'Dear Lord,' he mumbled in surprise. Then he picked up the toothbrush ... Only it had been eaten away until it was just a stub. My word, he thought, talk about extra-strength tartar control.

Now for the first time he noticed the card in the bag and took it out. Richie had written, *'Serva vitam! Statim effuge ungue vincula pasta dentali.'* Cadbury translated it in his head. *'Life in danger. Use toothpaste on bars.'*

He didn't notice the large prisoner with greasy hair and a long scar on his face, who had stepped quietly into the bathroom. The man was wearing black jeans, a black T-shirt and a black leather motorcycle jacket.

The butler frowned. *Life in danger?* Sounded a bit melodramatic, didn't it?

Without warning, two hands whipped a rolled towel around Cadbury's neck and began to choke him. Maybe the message wasn't so melodramatic after all, the butler thought, and instantly reacted with the defensive karate the Riches had had him trained in.

'Yah!' 'Ooof!' 'Ahh!' 'Ugh!' Thud! The scar-faced man's unconscious body crashed to the floor and Cadbury dusted his hands. Other than a throbbing black eye, he was unharmed.

'Never mess with a man who has sensitive teeth,' he said, and immediately started applying the 'toothpaste' to some bars covering a window that overlooked an alley.

Several minutes later, Cadbury, now dressed in his attacker's motorcycle clothes, pulled the bars off the window and climbed down to the alley below.

'Cadbury!' Richie ran out from behind a smelly green dumpster. He was still wearing sunglasses, tie-dyed T-shirt, and baggy jeans. 'What happened to your eye?'

'Just a scratch, Master Rich.'

Richie threw his arms around the butler and gave him an impulsive hug. 'You're all right!'

Cadbury hugged him back, then realized what he was doing and quickly let go.

'Excuse my familiarity, Master Rich,' he apologized. 'I was simply caught up in the moment. I didn't mean to –'

'Cadbury? Shut up!' Richie said with a big grin.

Cadbury looked at him and paled. 'Master Rich! Dear Lord! I'm away for a day or two and your taste descends into the gutter.'

'My taste?' Richie's jaw dropped. 'Look at *you*. Pretty radical, Cadbury.'

Cadbury felt ashamed as he looked down at the black T-shirt, jeans and leather jacket. 'Fortunately, I was able to retain my own underwear.'

Then Richie remembered the newspaper he'd found in the driveway that morning. 'Look at this!'

RICH WRECKAGE RECOVERED! blared the headline. Cadbury felt a pang shoot through his heart.

'Dear Lord, sir,' he said sadly. 'I'm so sorry.'

'Don't be,' Richie said excitedly. 'They found Mom and Dad's plane, but they *didn't* find any bodies. No life-raft either! Mom and Dad are alive! I *know* it!'

'Have you tried Dadlink?' Cadbury asked.

'We can't go back to the house now,' Richie said. Suddenly he had an idea. 'But I know what we can do! Come on!'

13

The tiny orange raft rocked in the smooth ocean waves. Mrs Rich woke from a fitful nap to find her husband working feverishly on the Dadlink. Pieces of the Lady Remington shaver lay all over the raft.

'Is it fixed yet?' Mrs Rich asked, shielding her eyes. The constant pounding of the sun gave her a headache.

'We'll soon see,' Mr Rich answered. 'I've used the battery and some of the parts from your shaver to jerry-rig something here. I can't dial out, but with some luck I might be able to get the homing signal to work.'

Using her nail-file, he tightened a screw on the tiny cellular phone. The Riches shared a hopeful look, then Mr Rich pressed a button on the phone's keypad. *Beep! Beep! Beep!*

'It's working!' his wife cried happily.

'As long as the power holds out,' her husband cautioned. 'And let's just hope Richie hasn't given up the search.'

'Richie? Of course he hasn't,' Mrs Rich said.

'Now, excuse me while I get changed.'

Mr Rich gave her a sceptical look.

'Really, darling,' his wife said, gesturing to her tattered and soiled clothes. 'If I'm going to be rescued, you can't expect me to let them see me dressed like *this*.'

A thousand miles away, at the Rich mansion, Van Dough stood in Professor Keenbean's lab and spoke on a cellular phone while Keenbean sat nearby under the watchful eye of Ferguson.

'I see,' Van Dough said in a monotone. 'Right, get back to me as soon as you hear anything.' He folded the phone closed and turned to the Professor. 'So, it appears the boy helped the butler escape from jail.'

'That's right!' Professor Keenbean snapped, crossing his arms obstinately. 'And I know *everything* about you. Everything! You hear me? And what I know will send you *both* to jail!'

Van Dough nodded calmly. 'Well, in that case I'm afraid we're just going to have to kill you.'

Professor Keenbean blinked and quickly changed his tune. 'Actually, I don't know *that* much. What do I know? Besides, who'd believe me anyway? I'm a loon. My own mother thinks I'm strange.'

'Shut up!' Van Dough yelled angrily as he paced around the lab, thinking.

'Uh, do you think I could go?' Professor Keenbean

asked, raising his hand. 'I just remembered I have a three o'clock appointment with my dentist.'

'You're not going anywhere, Professor Franken-bean,' Van Dough informed him. 'There's one thing I believe you do know that will be very helpful to us.'

'Ha!' Professor Keenbean laughed haughtily. 'You can forget it! I'm not helping you. I'm a loyal Rich family employee. No matter what you do — beat me, burn me, insert hot needles under my fingernails, I will never, *never*, talk.'

Van Dough nodded at Ferguson, who took out a gun and pointed it at Professor Keenbean.

'Er, did I say never?' The Professor swallowed nervously. 'Let me rephrase that . . .'

Meanwhile, Richie and Cadbury had caught a train to another part of town, where the house were small but well maintained, with neatly trimmed yards. Gloria lived here in an upstairs apartment. They managed to find it and rang the bell. Gloria came to the door.

'Yes?' she said, apparently not recognizing Richie in his hip-hop clothes, nor Cadbury as a biker desperado.

'Gloria, it's me,' Richie said, raising his sunglasses.

Gloria smiled. 'Cool new look, Richie.'

Her mother, Diane, came up behind her, saying, 'Gloria who're you talking to?' She saw Richie and Cadbury and grinned. 'Well, look who's slumming.'

Cadbury gave her a sheepish look, but Richie reached for the door. 'Gloria, I need to use your computer. It's real important.'

Gloria led them into the living-room. A large bulky old computer stood on a desk. 'I know it's pretty old,' she said. 'You're probably grossed out that you have to use it.'

'It's great,' Richie said, sitting down at it. 'This just might work.'

He got down to business and Gloria stood behind him and watched. 'Hmmm. Looks like I'm gonna have to write a small communications program so we can link up to my computer.'

'You can write computer programs?' Gloria asked, impressed.

'Yeah, I taught myself how last year,' Richie said.

'Wow.' Gloria thought for a moment. 'You know, when I first met you I thought you were just a spoiled rich kid. But now . . . I think you're not so bad.'

Richie winced at the backhanded compliment. 'Uh, thanks.'

'No, I mean it,' Gloria said. 'A lot of kids would've given up by now, but you —'

'That's because I know Mom and Dad are still alive,' Richie said as he typed. 'And I'm gonna find them.'

Meanwhile, in the kitchen, Diane took a cold slab of raw meat out of the refrigerator. 'Now hold still,' she said to Cadbury.

'Really, madam.' Cadbury backed away. 'This isn't necessary.'

Slap! Diane slapped the cold meat over his black and blue eye. Her face hardened. 'Look, I told you, don't call me madam.'

'Forgive me, Diane,' Cadbury corrected himself, then gazed out of the window and recited:

'Through the silver woods doth the Goddess roam,
Her bosom the ever-welcoming hunter's home,
Diana, Oh, mysterious Diana —'

'We give our Praise to thee.' Diane finished the poem for him. Cadbury looked shocked.

'Lord Byron, right?' Diane said with a smile.

'You . . . you're familiar with Byron?' Cadbury asked, amazed.

'Sure,' Diane said. 'I love poetry. So, uh, you like hockey?'

Before Cadbury could answer, Richie called to him from the living-room.

The butler joined Richie, who was staring intently at the computer.

'I think I've got it,' the boy said. 'I'm just about ready to try for contact.'

Richie typed his phone number into the communications program and waited while the modem forwarded the call. Moments later, the words 'Hello, Richie. May I help you?' appeared on Gloria's computer screen.

'I'm in!' Richie said excitedly, and typed 'Locate Dad.'

As always, the computer requested the secret password. Richie typed 'Slugger'.

'FATHER FOUND,' flashed on the screen.

'They're alive!' Richie cried happily.

14

Back at the mansion, Ferguson had tied Professor Keenbean to a chair and was standing behind it, choking the Professor with his own tie. Van Dough stood in front of Keenbean, smiling wickedly.

'I *told* you,' the Professor insisted. 'I don't know where the vault is.'

Van Dough rolled his eyes. 'Oh *please*, you can do better than that.'

'And even if I did,' the Professor wheezed, 'it wouldn't do you any good.'

Van Dough's eyebrows rose. 'And why, pray tell, is that?'

'The lock is voice-activated,' Keenbean explained. 'Only Mr or Mrs Rich can get in.'

Van Dough's face darkened and he glared at Keenbean with an icy grin. 'Unfortunately, Mr and Mrs Rich have been permanently detained. So you're going to have to come up with some other way for me to get into that vault.'

Just then a phone on the wall rang and Ferguson

answered it. 'What!? You're serious? I'll be right there.'

Ferguson raced up to Richie's room, where a security guard was staring at the boy's computer. The 'FATHER FOUND' message was flashing on the screen.

'When did this come on?' Ferguson asked.

'Just before I called you,' the security man said.

The words on the screen changed. Now it said, 'Exact coordinates will be pinpointed in ten seconds.'

Ferguson felt his eyes bulge. 'They *really* are alive!'

In eight seconds their exact whereabouts would be revealed. At first, the thought filled Ferguson with terror. Van Dough would have his head. But then he realized he was wrong. Van Dough would be delighted. Only who'd turned on the computer?

The kid! Ferguson looked down and saw the red lights on the modem flashing.

Four seconds . . .

Ferguson grabbed the modem and yanked it away from the computer, pulling the wires out. A few seconds later, the precise coordinates for locating Mr and Mrs Rich appeared on the computer screen. Ferguson scribbled them down. Then he picked up the phone and called his boss down in the lab.

'Mr Van Dough?' he said excitedly. 'I've got

great news! Looks like we've just found a way to get into the Rich family vault after all!'

In Gloria's living-room, the computer screen suddenly went blank. Richie's fingers scrambled over the keys, but the words 'ACCESS TERMINATED' flashed on the screen. His shoulders slumped and he shook his head sadly. 'I've been cut off.'

'How?' Diane asked.

'They must've pulled the modem.'

'But at least we're certain now *your* parents are alive!' Cadbury said happily.

'But where?' Richie asked.

15

That night, on a dark moonlit hill overlooking the estate, Richie peeked over a hedge and surveyed the grounds. Beside him, more heads popped up: Cadbury's, Diane's, Gloria's, Peewee's, Omar's, and finally, Tony's. They were all wearing backpacks and carrying walkie-talkies. Before them was the vast Rich lawn, brightly lit with halogen lamps.

'Uh-oh, check it out,' Peewee said. 'It's as bright as daytime!'

'And there are guards everywhere,' said Omar.

'I say, Master Rich,' Cadbury said nervously. 'I'm not sure about this at all.'

Seeing the brightly lit grounds and the guards, Richie felt his determination begin to ebb. He'd come up with a pretty good plan, but getting into the house was still going to be one tough job, and it was pretty likely someone was going to get caught or hurt.

'The Dadlink's in my room,' he said. 'It's the only way I can find out where my parents are and warn them about what's going on before Van Dough gets them. I have to go.'

Cadbury took a deep breath and let it out slowly. 'Well, I'm already wanted for attempted murder, escape *and* blowing up an aeroplane. Breaking and entering sounds *right* up my alley.'

Diane smiled proudly at him.

'Listen, everyone,' Richie whispered. 'If anyone wants to turn back, now's your chance.'

Everyone immediately said they were in. It was a far cry from the way Richie's 'friends' at school would have replied.

'Good,' Richie said. 'You all know what to do. Mrs Koscinski, you keep watch from here. Everyone else, move out.'

Trying to stay in the shadows as much as possible, the kids sneaked across a corner of the lawn towards the kid-a-pult. While Peewee and Tony went to get the 'ammo', Richie and the others silently pushed the kid-a-pult behind some bushes where it wouldn't be seen.

Moments later Tony and Peewee returned lugging heavy burlap sacks marked FERTILIZER.

'Here's the stuff from the gardener's shed,' Peewee grunted.

'It stinks, man,' Tony said, holding his nose.

'We better make this first shot count,' Cadbury warned the boys. 'It may be our last.'

Meanwhile, Richie went ahead to the bushes near

104

the closest guard, who was standing next to a statue of a Greek goddess and eating some Twinkies. Behind Richie, the kids and Cadbury loaded the first bag of fertilizer into the kid-a-pult.

'Ordnance in position,' Cadbury whispered.

'Ready,' Tony whispered into his walkie-talkie.

'OK,' Richie whispered into his walkie-talkie. 'Ready . . . Aim . . . *Fire!*'

Sproing! The kid-a-pult launched the bag of fertilizer. But just at that moment, the guard bent over to pick something up from the lawn.

Whomp! The bag of fertilizer smashed into the statue and knocked it over.

'Huh?' The guard straightened up and stared at the statue and the bag of fertilizer.

'We missed!' Richie screeched into the walkie-talkie. *'Reload! Reload!'*

The kids and Cadbury scrambled to reload the kid-a-pult with another bag of fertilizer.

'Ordnance ready!' Cadbury whispered.

'Fire two!' Richie ordered.

By now the guard had sniffed the statue and come to a startling conclusion. He grabbed his pocket radio. 'Security! This is Nash. Someone's throwing manure! Send —'

Thwack! The second bag of fertilizer smashed into him, knocking him out cold and leaving him covered in coarse brown animal by-product.

'Direct hit!' Richie cheered.

105

Watching through the night-binoculars from the lookout point, Diane picked up her walkie-talkie. 'All clear!'

'Tally-ho!' Cadbury called. He and the boys raced across the lawn to the fallen guard. Someone was trying to call the guard on his radio. 'Nash,' the voice said. 'Come in. Anything wrong?'

Cadbury scooped up the radio and spoke into it with a disguised voice. 'False alarm, boss. Everything's slicker'n snot on a doorknob.'

'Oh, OK,' the voice replied. 'Over and out.'

Richie gave Cadbury a high-five, then took a keycard out of the guard's pocket and dragged him behind some shrubs. Peewee spotted an unopened package of Twinkies on the ground and stuck it in his backpack. Tony gave him a look.

'Hey,' Peewee whispered defensively, 'spoils of war, man.'

Meanwhile, Omar leaned over the unconscious guard, who was covered with manure. 'Man, this dude stinks!'

'Come on.' Richie led them around to a little-used side entrance into the mansion. Using the keycard, he opened the door and they went in. Richie led them down some dark stairs to the basement.

He led them down a dark hallway. As they passed Professor Keenbean's lab, they heard strange grunts and moans coming from inside.

'Mmmmmm . . . Uhhhhhh . . . Ahhhhhhh . . .'

106

'Hold up a second,' Richie whispered to the others. He cautiously pushed open the door to the lab and flicked on a flashlight.

Inside, Professor Keenbean was tied to a chair. On his armrest was a liverwurst sandwich. The noises had come from the Professor as he strained towards the sandwich!

'Keenbean!' Richie and the others started to untie him. Richie took hold of the piece of tape covering the Professor's arms and ripped it off.

'Yeeoooowww!' Keenbean screamed in pain and Richie had to slap his hand over his mouth.

'Quiet,' Richie hissed, letting go.

'You wouldn't believe what those animals did to me!' Keenbean cried. 'It was inhuman!'

'Where's Van Dough?' Richie asked.

'He was in the middle of torturing me when he got a phone call,' the Professor said. 'Then he ran out laughing, giggling and rubbing his hands together with glee ... You know, Richie, he's not a nice person.'

Richie didn't have time to discuss Van Dough's personality traits. 'Listen to me, Keenbean. We have to get up to my room. We need you to create a diversion so we can get past the guards. Can you do something?'

Keenbean thought for a moment, then grinned and twirled his moustache. Only he didn't *have* a moustache! 'I think I can whip something up.'

Richie turned to Gloria. 'You go with him. Omar, Tony and Peewee, you know what to do?'

The boys nodded grimly.

'OK,' Richie said. 'Let's do it!'

Following a map Richie had drawn, the boys soon found themselves in a basement utility room, surrounded by enormous clusters of wires.

'Looks like the security and TV cable systems for the house are both wired through here,' Omar said, fishing out two identical white cables.

'Which is which?' Tony asked.

'You've got me,' Omar said with a shrug.

'Then we better do them both,' Peewee said.

Omar quickly stripped the insulation off the cables and held up the bare wires.

'OK,' Peewee said, 'now we wait for Richie's word.'

Meanwhile, Keenbean led Gloria through a basement hallway and stopped next to a large pipe.

'What's this?' Gloria asked.

'Richie said they needed a diversion,' the Professor replied, unscrewing a plug in the pipe and pouring in some white powder. 'This is a combination laundry detergent, dishwasher soap and bubble bath. I call it Sudsational.'

'But why are you pouring it in here?' Gloria asked.

'Because this is the pipe to all the fountains,' Keenbean explained. 'Right now every fountain on the estate is starting to foam into a mountain of suds.'

Gloria nodded. 'That's an interesting diversion.'

From another window, Richie saw guards outside engulfed in huge waves of foam. That Keenbean was a genius! He grabbed his walkie-talkie. 'OK, kill the cameras now!'

In the basement, Omar touched the bare wires together.

'All right, guys!' he said anxiously. 'The camera's are down! Go for broke!'

16

In the den upstairs, Van Dough reclined in a leather chair and watched a movie on TV. The phone rang and he picked it up. 'Yes, Ferguson, do you have the package? Good. Bring it up here.'

He hung up and smiled, then unwrapped a hefty Havana cigar and placed it between his lips. A security guard lit it for him and Van Dough took a satisfied puff. Despite some minor pitfalls, things were going very, very well.

Suddenly, the movie on the TV disappeared and the Three Stooges came on, accompanied by the Three Stooges music. Van Dough sat up straight in his chair.

Brriiinnngg! The phone rang again and Van Dough grabbed it. 'What?'

'It's Zullo in the security control room,' a panicked voice said.

'Don't tell me,' Van Dough moaned.

'Every TV monitor down here is showing the Three Stooges!' Zullo said excitedly. 'I have no idea what's going on. But we could have an intruder.'

Instead of going berserk, Van Dough settled back into his chair and smiled, oddly confident. 'Perfect timing, Zullo,' he said. 'Secure the perimeter.'

Not far away, Richie and Cadbury had gone up the stairs to the second floor and raced down the hall to Richie's room. The room was dark, and Cadbury reached for the light switch.

Richie hurried to his computer and started it.

'LOCATE FATHER,' he ordered, and quickly typed the secret password.

'FATHER FOUND,' the computer quickly announced and a red light flashed on the map.

In the dark, Richie frowned. That can't be right, he thought, and typed in a request for the precise latitude and longitude. They came back and Richie shook his head and sat back, confused.

'What is it, Master Rich?' Cadbury asked, looking over the boy's shoulder at the computer screen. 'What's wrong?'

'The coordinates,' Richie said. 'It says Mom and Dad are *here*. Right inside the house.'

Flash! Suddenly the lights went on. Richie and Cadbury wheeled around. Ferguson was standing at the light switch, holding a gun.

On the other side of the room stood Laurence Van Dough. And on the bed beside him sat Mr and Mrs Rich, tied up.

'Welcome home, slugger,' Van Dough said with a

wicked smile. 'You were even quicker than I thought you'd be.'

'Mom! Dad!' Richie raced towards them, giving them both a hug.

'Why, you!' Cadbury made a lunge towards Van Dough, but Ferguson aimed the gun at him.

'Now, now, Herbert.' Van Dough wagged a finger at him. 'Where's that famous British reserve?'

'Are you OK?' Richie asked his parents. 'Have they hurt you?'

Mr and Mrs Rich could only shake their heads.

Meanwhile, Van Dough checked his watch. 'Our other guests should be arriving any moment now.'

Richie realized he must have been talking about Diane and the kids. The whole thing had been a trap! And he'd led everyone into it!

Van Dough pulled Mrs and Mrs Rich to their feet.

'What do you want from us, Laurence?' Mr Rich asked.

'You mean, *besides* wealth, revenge and a bigger office?' Van Dough asked. 'I want the *vault*. The Rich family vault.'

Mr and Mrs Rich exchanged a look. Then Mr Rich looked back at Van Dough and acted surprised. '*That's* what this is all about?'

'Yes!' Van Dough shouted. 'The vault. Now where is it?'

Since he was still tied up, Mr Rich could only gesture towards the window with his chin. 'There.'

'Where?' Van Dough stared out of the window at the lit-up grounds.

'Right there,' Mr Rich said simply.

Van Dough stared outside where Mount Rich-more stood, shimmering in the moonlight.

'Mount *Richmore*?' he gasped in awe. 'Your vault's the *whole* mountain?'

'Well –' Mr Rich started to say.

'Oh, you must be *filthy* rich!' Van Dough cried with glee. He turned back to Mr Rich. 'Now, if you cooperate and get me in the vault, no one gets hurt.'

Mr Rich nodded. There was nothing else he could do.

'Good,' Van Dough said. 'Now take them away.'

Several security guards led the Riches out of the room. When they were gone, Van Dough turned to Ferguson. 'About little Richie and his friends. It's time they disappeared.'

'But I thought you just promised his parents –' Ferguson began.

'When have you ever known me to keep a promise?' Van Dough snapped. 'Now do it!'

After they'd finished overriding the security system, Professor Keenbean sent the kids back outside to rejoin Diane. He told them he'd rejoin them as soon as he'd 'picked up a few things'.

Then he returned to his lab and began stuffing some of his smaller inventions into a suitcase.

'I'm not letting all these inventions fall into the wrong hands,' he said to himself, as he grabbed the mechanical bee control and shoved it into the pocket of his lab coat. 'I've worked too hard –'

Slam! The doors to the lab burst open, and Ferguson and another security guard stepped in with Richie, Cadbury, Diane and the kids. Professor Keenbean barely had time to duck behind a lab table, unseen.

'Fine chief of security *you* turned out to be,' Cadbury said in disgust, as Ferguson pushed him into the lab.

'Guess I won't be winning that employee of the month award, huh?' Ferguson said with a smirk.

They were marched past the table where Keenbean was hiding. Ferguson pushed Cadbury and the others towards a metal stairway.

'Now, listen,' Cadbury said, digging in his heels, 'we *refuse* to go any farther.'

Ferguson jammed his gun in the butler's back. 'Get up those stairs!'

As Cadbury reluctantly started up the stairs, Keenbean peeked out from his hiding place. Oh, no! he thought. Ferguson was forcing them towards the huge bucket that fed the Sub-Atomic Molecular

114

Reorganizer! He was going to scramble their molecules!

The little crowd reached the top of the metal ladder. 'OK, all of you, into the bucket,' Ferguson ordered.

'Hey, you can't be serious,' Tony protested.

'Yeah, I don't like heights,' said Omar.

'Is this really necessary?' asked Diane.

Bang! Ferguson fired his gun at the ceiling.

'OK, everyone,' Tony said in a trembling voice, 'let's get in the bucket. No big deal. We're in the bucket.'

Still hiding behind the lab table, Keenbean knew he had to think of something fast. But what? In desperation, he opened the suitcase and searched through it. Hmmm, now here was something, he thought, bringing out a paint-can marked ADHESIVE x and a paint-brush.

Richie also knew what Ferguson had in mind for them. He stopped at the top of the stairs, but Ferguson prodded him with his gun. 'All aboard, *Master* Rich.'

On his hands and knees, Keenbean was crawling across the floor as fast as he could. The handle of the paint-can was in his teeth and the brush was in his pocket. He reached the bottom of the metal stairs, prised off the top of the can, and quickly began to paint the black adhesive on to the lower steps and handrail.

115

Meanwhile, everyone huddled together in the bucket, trading worried looks.

'Something tells me this ain't the Pirates of the Caribbean ride,' Omar said nervously.

Ferguson lowered a hinged mesh screen over the top of the bucket so that the kids couldn't escape. Then, with the other security guard leading the way, he started back down the stairs. Suddenly, near the bottom, the other guard's feet stuck to the steps and wouldn't move.

'Hey, what is this?' He tried to pull his hands off the railing, but they were stuck too. 'Help! I'm stuck!'

It didn't take long for Ferguson to figure out what had happened. 'So, it's the wacky Professor,' he said, vaulting over the side of the stairs to avoid the adhesive. 'Hey, Greenbean, I know you're in here!'

'It's Keenbean!' Richie told the others inside the bucket.

'Great.' Gloria rolled her eyes in despair.

'Hey,' Richie said. 'The guy's a genius. He'll save us.'

At that very moment, Keenbean was painting adhesive on the floor near the control board of the Molecular Reorganizer. He scurried around a corner just as Ferguson came around the table. The chief of security looked like he was going to walk right to the control board, but just before he got to the adhesive, he stopped and looked down.

'Nice try, Professor,' he said, seeing the sticky adhesive on the floor, 'but you're gonna have to do better than that.' Ferguson nimbly stepped around the adhesive and pressed the start button on the control board. The Molecular Reorganizer began to hum and the bucket jerked into motion.

'Guess what, Professor?' Ferguson yelled with glee. 'In thirty seconds you won't even recognize your little friends any more!'

Keenbean knew he was right. It was now or never! Looking around desperately for some way to save them, he spotted the laundry basket filled with dirty towels and lab coats. It wasn't much, but it was the only chance he had. Keenbean reached out, grabbed a towel, and quickly poured the adhesive on it.

With his gun drawn, Ferguson was walking carefully around the lab tables, searching for Keenbean. 'Come out, come out, Professor! Don't you want to join your friends?'

'Matter of fact, I do,' Keenbean said, jumping up behind him. As Ferguson whirled around, the Professor hurled the towel into his face.

'Ahhhh!' Ferguson screamed and tried to rip the towel off.

Bang! Bang! Bang! He fired wildly and stumbled about, blinded. Mustering his courage, Keenbean crept up from behind with a mallet.

Thunk! He bashed it over Ferguson's head, knocking him out cold.

'Wacky professor, huh?' Keenbean said, standing victoriously over the security chief. Then he remembered Richie and the others and hurried towards the control board.

'Ooops!' Keenbean looked down in horror as he realized he'd stepped into his own trap. His feet were stuck in the black adhesive! The only way out was to untie his shoes and step out of them. The overweight Professor groaned and bent over.

'Whoa!' he cried out as he lost his balance and fell backward.

Splat! He landed with his butt on the adhesive!

Across the lab, the bucket was just a few yards from the mouth of the giant machine.

'Hey, Professor!' Richie shouted from inside. 'Cutting it kind of close, aren't you?'

'I'm stuck!' Keenbean cried back. 'I can't get to the button!'

In the bucket, Richie and the others exchanged horrified looks.

'Some genius,' Gloria grumbled bitterly.

17

It was hopeless. Keenbean couldn't get to the button to turn off the machine. The kids would be dropped any second and come out the other end looking like bowling balls. Just then Keenbean remembered what was in his pocket. The remote control for the Robo-bee!

He yanked it out and switched it on. Not far away, the second Robo-bee buzzed to life and rose out of its glass box.

The huge bucket was almost right over the opening in the Molecular Reorganizer!

Keenbean frantically worked the controls for the Robo-bee. It shot around the room, diving, bombing and rolling this way and that.

'C'mon, darn it!' Keenbean shouted in frustration. 'Fly, my little pretty! Fly as you've never flown before!'

Clank! The bucket stopped over the machine, and the hinged bottom doors began to creak open. Inside, the kids and adults grabbed for anything they could hold on to.

'Well, I guess this is it,' Peewee cried.

'Master Rich,' Cadbury said sadly. 'It has indeed been a pleasure serving you.'

'What's going to happen to us?' Diane gasped.

'Well, most likely we'll all become bowling balls,' Richie said.

Across the room, Keenbean finally got the Robo-bee under control and sent it straight into Ferguson's behind. The stunned security man ran into the control knob and accidentally shut it off.

The hinged doors of the bucket froze in a partially open position.

'What happened?' Omar asked.

'Keenbean saved us!' Richie shouted with joy. 'I *told* you he's a genius!'

A few miles away, Van Dough and a security guard named Murdoch forced the Riches along a dark wooded path at gunpoint. Soon they reached a spot at the foot of the mountain where two boulders stood. Mr Rich pulled on the tree branch growing out of the rocks. One of the boulders rolled aside, revealing a metal lift door.

'Amazing!' Van Dough said. They got on the lift and the doors closed.

It was difficult to judge how far they travelled in the lift, but Van Dough had the feeling they were going up, not down. The lift finally stopped and the doors opened to reveal a long cavelike passageway. At the end was a huge vault door.

'OK,' Van Dough said, gesturing with his gun. 'Open it.'

Mr Rich gave his wife a questioning look. She nodded back. He stepped towards the wall beside the vault and flipped up a small plastic window, revealing a voice print apparatus.

'For access, please say code words now,' an electronic voice in the apparatus said.

'Ahem.' Mr and Mrs Rich sang, 'Side by side'.

'You've *got* to be kidding,' Van Dough grumbled.

But a split second later the computer voice said, 'Access approved, Mr Rich.'

Clang! The huge locking mechanism disengaged and the massive vault door opened. Inside, thick steel bars rose and an entire brick wall slid away, revealing ... a living-room wall, complete with bookshelves and a fireplace with crossed swords hanging over it.

'What's going on?' Van Dough asked with a scowl.

But a moment later the fireplace swung open like a door, revealing a vast room ... Only it didn't look like the inside of a vault. It looked like the inside of someone's *attic* ... filled with baby pictures, comic books, baseball cards, train sets, Lego, bowling trophies and all sorts of other stuff.

'I never dreamed,' Van Dough said in awe as he looked around. 'This is incredible! This is fantastic! This is junk.'

He turned to Mr and Mrs Rich and stared at them with a bewildered look. 'Baby pictures? Baseball cards? What is this?'

Mrs Rich lovingly picked up a bowling trophy and turned to his wife. 'Remember this?'

'Our first date,' his wife replied wistfully.

'But what is this?' Van Dough spluttered.

'Our most priceless possessions,' Mr Rich replied simply. 'That's what you put in a vault, right?'

'But what about the gold?' Van Dough asked, flabbergasted. 'The diamonds? The negotiable bearer bonds? The money! *Where's the money?*'

'In banks,' Mrs Rich replied as if it was obvious. 'You don't think we'd keep it here where someone like you could steal it, do you?'

'This . . . this can't be true,' Van Dough gasped, aiming his gun at the Riches. 'It's gotta be some kind of joke. Are you telling me there isn't one single solitary gold bar or emerald or thousand dollar bill in this whole *mountain?*'

'Sorry to disappoint you, Laurence,' Mr Rich replied. 'But that's not what we treasure.'

'Shoot them!' Van Dough screamed at the guard named Murdoch. 'Shoot them!'

Murdoch hesitated. 'Here? Now?'

'Yes!' Van Dough screamed. *'Shoot them right now!'*

18

In the confusion that followed their rescue from the Sub-Atomic Molecular Reorganizer, Cadbury ordered Diane to take the children and go immediately to the police.

'Aren't you coming?' Diane asked.

'No, I must stay here,' Cadbury replied stiffly.

'Herb.' Diane touched his sleeve. 'Be careful.'

'Hey!' Gloria cried behind them. 'Where's Richie?'

Everyone looked around. Richie was nowhere to be seen. Across the lab, Keenbean struggled to his feet, wearing boxer shorts and socks. His trousers and shoes were still stuck to the floor.

'My suitcase of inventions!' he cried. 'It's gone!'

Not far away, Ferguson staggered around and grabbed the towel with both hands.

Riiippp! He tore it off his face, taking some skin with it.

'The kid!' the security guard glued to the staircase shouted at him. 'I think he's going to the vault!'

Ferguson stumbled towards the door.

'Hey!' shouted the security guard. 'What about

123

me? You're not just gonna leave me? Hey!'

Ferguson disappeared through the door and the security guard turned to Cadbury and the others. 'Believe me,' he muttered, 'this ain't worth eight dollars twenty-five an hour.'

Carrying Keenbean's suitcase full of inventions, Richie roared towards Mount Richmore on his motorbike. He reached the tree branch sticking out of the rocks and yanked it open. The boulder rolled away and a moment later he was riding up in the lift.

Richie stepped out of the lift and saw that the huge vault door was open. They must be inside! He quietly crept through the door, past the metal bars and the sliding brick wall. As he passed the fake living-room fireplace, he noticed the crossed swords above the mantel.

Hmmm, he thought, taking one down. This might come in handy.

Suddenly he heard someone yell, 'Shoot them!' It was coming from an open vault door! Richie stepped into the doorway and saw his parents with Van Dough and Murdoch.

'Shoot them!' Van Dough shouted again.

'What's the matter, Mr Van Dough?' Richie asked. 'Can't you do it yourself?'

They all spun around.

'Richie!' his mother cried. 'Get out of here! Now!'

But her son took a step towards Van Dough and

124

said calmly, 'It's OK, Mom. I'm not afraid of him.' He took another step. 'He doesn't have the guts to shoot anyone. Do you, Mr Van Dough?'

Van Dough's face darkened. 'You're right. Well, generally you're right . . .' He raised his gun. 'But in this case I'll make an exception.'

'Richie!' Mrs Rich shouted.

Blam! Blam! Blam! Van Dough emptied his gun at Richie.

'Oh, my God!' Mrs Rich cried out.

But when the smoke cleared, Richie was still standing. Van Dough's jaw dropped and he looked down at his gun. Richie was about to take another step when *Riiipppp!* the front of his jacket tore away and clattered to the floor.

'Good old Stain-Away,' Mr Rich said with a smile.

Richie sprang into action, using his sword to knock the gun out of Van Dough's hand. Mr Rich lunged at Murdoch and wrestled him to the ground. Using his fencing moves, Richie duelled with Van Dough, who fought back with a bowling trophy.

Mrs Rich grabbed a banjo and swung it at Murdoch.

Bonk! The security guard went down in a heap.

'Yah!' With one final thrust, Richie drove Van Dough backwards.

Crash! The villain fell into a shelf of heavy trophies and they cascaded down around him.

'Run!' Mr Rich shouted. Richie and his parents tore out of the vault.

'We'll lock 'em in, Dad!' Richie shouted as he ran.

'Good idea, son,' Mr Rich shouted back.

They got out through the main vault door and Mr Rich shouted, 'Close door!'

'Yes, Mr Rich,' the computerized voice replied. 'Have a nice day.'

The Riches raced down the passageway towards the lift.

Blam! Blam! Ping! Pang! Bullets suddenly ricocheted off the walls around them. Richie and his parents whirled around to see Van Dough behind them! He squeezed through the vault door just as it closed!

Trapped in the passageway, Richie knew they'd be sitting ducks.

'I know another way out!' Mr Rich shouted and started to run down an adjoining passageway.

Blam! Blam! Van Dough followed, shooting at them.

Cool night air drifted towards them as they ran. The Riches raced down the passageway and found themselves high on the side of the mountain, illuminated by the moonlight.

'Oh, no!' Mrs Rich suddenly stopped. 'We're in your ear!'

Richie and his father looked around and realized she was right. They were standing in Mr Rich's earhole!

Blam! Ping! A bullet ricocheted above them.

Mr Rich pointed down. 'Climb down that way!'

They started to climb out of the huge stone ear and down the earlobe. The stone was cool and rough and they had to be careful not to lose their grip.

Ker-pow! suddenly a bright red laser beam struck the rock beside them, blasting a large crater.

'Ferguson's shooting the rock-cutting laser at us!' Mr Rich shouted.

Blam! Ping! Another bullet ricocheted from above. Richie looked up and saw Van Dough aiming his gun at them from Mr Rich's ear.

They couldn't go up and they couldn't go down. There was only one other possible way to escape.

'Across the faces!' Mr Rich shouted. In the moon-light Richie jumped on to a workmen's platform that stretched across Mr Rich's cheek. His parents scurried behind him.

Blam! Ping! Another bullet narrowly missed them.

'Take cover behind my nose!' Mr Rich shouted.

They ran to the end of the platform and then, one by one, crawled over the bridge of Mr Rich's nose.

Ker-pow! Another laser shot disintegrated the top of Mr Rich's eyeglasses, sending shattered scraps of rock raining down on them.

Blam! Ping! Van Dough fired another bullet, chipping away a piece of Mr Rich's nose. Richie looked over the bridge of his father's nose and saw Van Dough on the platform, coming towards them.

Whack! Whack! Using his sword, Richie quickly hacked at the ropes holding the closest end of the platform.

Crash! The platform fell away, making it impossible for the villain to come any closer. Seeing that his way was cut off, Van Dough quickly backtracked and disappeared. Richie hardly had time to wonder where he was going when . . .

Ker-pow! Another blast from the laser gun smashed into the lower rim of Mr Rich's eyeglasses, breaking it off.

'Richaaaard!' Mrs Rich screamed as she lost her grip and started to slide down Mr Rich's nose.

'Mom!' Richie cried out, and reached down to grab her wrist. But now he started to lose *his* grip.

'Dad!' he shouted, 'I can't hold on!'

Mr Rich grabbed his son's wrist. Now all three of them hung precariously like a human chain.

'Hold on, darling!' Mr Rich shouted. 'I'm going to swing you into my mouth!'

He swung them over and Mrs Rich got a foothold on her husband's upper lip. Richie let go and she climbed down into her husband's mouth.

'Richie!' she shouted back up. 'Slide down and I'll catch you!'

On the ground below, Ferguson aimed the laser

rock cutter at them. 'This should be like swattin' flies,' he chuckled fiendishly.

'Pardon me,' a voice said in the dark.

Ferguson spun around just in time to see Cadbury crash a scale model of Mount Richmore over his head. The security chief crumpled to the ground in a heap.

'Well,' Cadbury said, dusting his hands. 'That was smashing.'

Wham! Ferguson's fist caught him by surprise. The two men started to wrestle, banging against the laser gun and making it fire wildly.

Ker-pow! Mrs Rich's left ear disintegrated.

Ker-pow! Richie's nose disappeared in a puff of rock and dust.

Richie slid down into his father's mouth. A moment later Mr Rich joined them.

Ker-pow! A laser blast smashed into one of Mr Rich's stone teeth, leaving an unsightly gap.

'Looks like I'm going to need major bridgework after this,' Richie's father joked.

Ker-pow! Another blast smashed away half of Mrs Rich's nose, narrowing it considerably.

'My nose!' she gasped. 'I look like Michael Jackson!'

Ker-pow! A blast dented her chin.

'My chin!' she said. 'He put a cleft in my chin!'

'Hey, it worked for Kirk Douglas,' her husband reminded her.

Wham! Down below, Cadbury connected with Ferguson's jaw and the security chief fell backwards. The laser stopped firing and pointed skyward.

Meanwhile, using ropes from the platform, Van Dough tied a length around his waist and lowered himself down Mr Rich's face. He hoped to get a clean shot at the Riches inside Mr Rich's mouth.

Down below, Ferguson jumped to his feet and whipped out a flick-knife. The knife's razor-sharp blade glinted in the pale moonlight.

'Well,' Cadbury huffed, 'so you don't want to play fair.'

Ferguson lunged at Cadbury, who ducked and swung the barrel of the laser gun like a baseball bat.

Clunk! The barrel smashed into Ferguson's head and the chief of security went down.

'Game, set and match,' Cadbury said, dusting his hands once again. Then he turned and aimed the laser gun at Mount Richmore.

Van Dough was standing on Mr Rich's eyeglass frame.

Ker-pow! Cadbury fired the laser and the rock under Van Dough's feet crumbled away.

'Yikes!' Van Dough slid down to the tip of Mr Rich's nose. Then the rope tightened and held him there. The villain swung back and forth from the nose. Below him was a straight drop of two hundred feet.

From Mr Rich's mouth, the Riches watched Van Dough dangle in front of them.

'Help me! Help me!' he cried desperately.

'Hey, Dad,' Richie said. 'Looks like you got a bug on your nose.'

'I think we should squash it,' Mrs Rich said.

'Please!' Van Dough begged and cried. 'Help me! I'll make it up to you! Please!'

Mr Rich turned to his wife. 'Darling, you do the honours.'

Wham! Mrs Rich reached back and let go a swing, smashing Van Dough right in the face. The villain was knocked out cold. Richie turned to his father.

'Dad,' he said. 'I *know* what company policy says and I *know* how you feel about firing people, but –'

His father nodded. 'Well, Richie, in this case I think we can make the exception. Why don't you do the honours?'

'Mr Van Dough,' Richie said, 'you're fired.'

'Well done, son.' Mr Rich patted him on the back.

It wasn't long before the police and the media arrived. Van Dough, Ferguson and the security guards were handcuffed and led to police cars.

Nearby Richie stood with his parents and watched.

131

'It's really great having you guys back,' he said, giving them each a hug.

'We've missed you too, son,' his father said.

'*Rooof!*' Dollar barked and Mrs Rich reached down to pet him. 'Of course, Dollar, we've missed you, too.'

Cadbury joined them and took on his usual reserved manner. 'May I say that seeing you all together again as a family, alive and well, fills me with an emotion that I find hard to express.'

The butler suddenly threw decorum to the wind and embraced Richie happily.

'That wasn't so hard, was it, Cadbury?' Richie asked with a grin.

As if there was no stopping him now, Cadbury turned and hugged both Mr and Mrs Rich. 'Welcome home,' he said happily.

'Seems like you two had quite an adventure while we were gone,' Mr Rich said after the butler let go.

'And *where* did you get those clothes, Cadbury?' Mrs Rich asked.

'Master Rich and I *did* have a bit of a "walk on the wild side" if you please,' Cadbury allowed. 'But I assure you that our attire will be returned to normal by tomorrow.'

'Aw, nuts.' Richie scuffed his day-glo hi-tops on the ground.

'Well, I think Richie looks perfectly normal to

me,' Mr Rich said. 'And Cadbury, it looks like you've finally loosened the cork a little, too.'

Richie grinned, but the butler scoffed at the thought.

'*Sir*, I assure you that I am the same conservative, sober retainer that you have always known,' he said. 'And that reminds me, there's something I've been meaning to speak to you about.'

'What is it, Cadbury?' Mr Rich asked.

Instead of answering, the butler just pointed back at Mount Richmore. Richie and his parents turned.

'Oh, dear!' Mrs Rich groaned. The wild laser shots had transformed the faces of Richie and his parents into . . . the Three Stooges.

'Now *that* I like,' Mr Rich said with a grin.

19

Some time later, the kids were back at the Rich estate, playing baseball on the front lawn. Richie, wearing a United Tool Tiger uniform, waited on a pitch. It was the last innings. The score was tied and there were two outs.

Crack! Richie smacked the ball into deep left field. The ball rolled over the grass, bounced off a bag of fertilizer and came to rest against a pair of legs held at the ankle with chains. The legs belonged to Ferguson.

Beside him stood Van Dough. They were both in chains and wearing prison outfits. A prison guard stood near them.

Ferguson looked back at the field. 'Good hit.'

'Shut up,' Van Dough said in disgust while he leaned on a shovel.

Ferguson got back to work, spreading manure over the garden. 'Aren't you going to help me?'

'What's the rush?' Van Dough asked with a shrug. 'We're only going to be doing this for another seven thousand four hundred and ninety-three days.'

Back at the field, Diane and Mr and Mrs Rich cheered as Richie rounded the bases and slid into home plate under Peewee's tag.

'Point scored!' shouted Cadbury, who was dressed as the umpire. Richie gave him a look. 'Oops.' Cadbury grinned. 'I meant, safe!'

The kids on Richie's team rushed towards him, cheering enthusiastically. They lifted him to their shoulders and paraded him around the bases. Richie's grin was broad and filled with delight.

'Not bad, ump,' Diane said, giving Cadbury a peck on the cheek.

Cadbury arched his eyebrow. 'You're not so bad yourself, madam.'

Diane's eyes narrowed. 'Don't call me —'

Before she could get the words out, Cadbury took her in his arms and kissed her.

'Yeah!' the kids all cheered, laughing together. Richie was still up on their shoulders.

Nearby, Richie's parents watched fondly.

'You know,' Mr Rich mused. 'I can honestly say that for once Richie really *is* the richest boy in the world.'

He and his wife smiled at each other and watched as the kids carried Richie off . . . to their very own McDonald's.

Some other Puffin titles to enjoy

RICHIE RICH: THE FILM STORYBOOK
Nancy E. Krulik
*Adapted by Nancy E. Krulik from the screenplay
written by Tom S. Parker & Jim Jennewein*

It's tough being a billionaire boy. Richie Rich just wants to play baseball with Peewee, Omar, Gloria and Tony. But instead he has to run his dad's business, rescue his parents and save the family fortune! It's just another normal day for Richie Rich!

MADAME DOUBTFIRE
Anne Fine

A vast apparition towered over her on the doorstep. It wore a loose salmon pink coat . . . and tucked under its arm was an enormous imitation crocodile skin handbag . . . 'I'm Madame Doubtfire, dear.'

Lydia, Christopher and Natalie Hilliard are used to domestic turmoil and have been torn between their warring parents ever since the divorce. But all that changes when their mother takes on a most unusual cleaning lady.

Despite her extraordinary appearance, Madame Doubtfire turns out to be a talented and efficient housekeeper and, for a short time at least, the arrangement is a resounding success. But, as the Hilliard children soon discover, there's more to Madame Doubtfire than domestic talents . . .